7. 99

INCR
YO
ENF

Louis Proto

INCREASE YOUR ENERGY

Regain

your zest

for life

the natural

way

PIATKUS

© 1991 Louis Proto

This edition published in 1998

First published in 1991 by
Judy Piatkus (Publishers) Ltd of
5 Windmill Street, London W1P 1HF

*A catalogue record for this book is available from
the British Library*

ISBN 0–7499–1821–7

Set in Linotron Baskerville by
Phoenix Photosetting, Chatham, Kent
Printed and bound in Great Britain by
Mackays of Chatham PLC, Chatham, Kent

CONTENTS

ACKNOWLEDGMENTS

I am indebted for much of the information on electro-magnetic pollution in Chapter 8 to John Davidson's excellent *Subtle Energy* (C. W. Daniel Company Limited, 1987). My thanks are also due to The Bach Centre, England, for permission to list the flower remedies.

FOREWORD

It was in the early 1970s, when training in holistic therapies, that I first began to learn about the ways of energy. The therapists who taught us were mainly Americans who had come out to London from Esalen, the world's first (and largest) 'growth centre' at Big Sur in California.

They initiated us into a whole new way of understanding and working with energy: what makes people 'tick', and what makes them sick – and how and why they get well again; how to have more zest and create quality of life; how to achieve clarity, both in relation to ourselves and in interpersonal transactions; and of the connection between mind and body.

Each of these therapists had their own approach, for example, Gestalt, bioenergetics, rolfing, different forms of massage, Felden-kreis, psychosynthesis and so on. But basically they all spoke the same language – that of energy, awareness and responsibility. It was a time of immense growth for me, sometimes humbling, often enlightening, always empowering.

Since those days I have been keen to learn more. And the more one learns, the more there is to learn, for the subject is as vast as it is fasci-nating. My search has taken me far and wide and through other disciplines, including training in 'conventional' psychotherapy, Taoist therapeutics, the world of Zen, and practising yoga and medi-tation for three years in an Indian ashram.

This book is about quality of life, about how to feel better than you do, how to recognise and satisfy your needs, working with your own energy and bringing more awareness to your own process. For ulti-mately, energy processes are what we are.

Louis Proto
October 1990

1

ENERGYWISE

We human beings are energy transformers. We take it in, process it, and put it out again when, for example, we speak, move, work, play, relate, make love. How much energy we have available, and the quality of the energy we express in our lives depends to a very large extent on what we have taken in. Our bodies, like our cars, respond to our treatment of them. If they are to produce the energy we want from them we must be careful to make sure we are eating well and the right sort of food, breathing efficiently, and not runnning ourselves into the ground through overwork and other forms of stress. We have to learn ways of replenishing our store of energy, and be sensitive to our energy levels so that we know when we are overdoing things and need to recharge our batteries.

But we are more than just our bodies. Our mental, emotional and physical energies are inextricably linked. It is one energy system. What happens to us on a psychological plane is immediately reflected in physiological changes. What this means is that our energy levels will also be affected by our state of mind, the ways in which we relate to others, whether we are enjoying life or having a hard time. Negativity from others will certainly bring us down, the experience of being loved will boost our energy. But even more important is to love ourselves, for a negative self-image is perhaps the biggest single drain on our energy that there is. What we tell ourselves is supremely important for our wellbeing. If we are constantly criticising ourselves we castrate our energy: we lose all sense of zest or joy and the quality of our lives goes down the drain.

It has been estimated that about 70% of patients who find their way into the consulting rooms of general practitioners complain of tiredness, lack of energy, feeling unable to cope and vaguely depressed. In the absence of actual evidence of something wrong with their bodies that can show up on an X-ray or other tests however, there is little the doctor can do to make them feel better, short of prescribing tranquillisers and telling them to take things easier. Which is not to say that if fatigue is persistent one should not check out with one's doctor whether something is organically wrong, for fatigue is often one of the warning signs of incipient illness. Most often however, lacking energy is a concomitant of the hectic life-styles that we lead today which impose stress on our systems, physically, mentally and emotionally.

Stress drains us, and long-standing stress is increasingly recognised by medical authorities as one of the biggest single causes of the so-called 'stress diseases' which include not only the obvious ones like disorders of the digestive system (eg stomach and duodenal ulcers), back pain, heart trouble and high blood pressure, but are now thought to include the depression of our immune systems that can predispose us to cancer and AIDS.

Often we may not be aware of just how much stress we are under. When we say that somebody is 'under stress' we usually mean that he or she is working too hard, is coping with loss of a loved one through separation, divorce or death, or struggling to make ends meet. But research has shown that virtually anything can be stressful for some people, including getting married, moving house, going on holiday – and even Christmas. There are many other ways in which we leak energy which are only just becoming recognised, especially for those of us who live and work in big cities. The sheer pace of life, the constant background of traffic noise, increasing inner-city violence – all serve to make us tense. We are subjected to a relentless barrage of advertising aimed at conditioning us to the idea that if we don't have this or that car, these clothes, this hi-fi system, we are not OK, 'with it'. The price we have to pay for these things is not just the one on the price tag: we have to work harder, be more competitive, wheel and deal to make sure we keep up with the Joneses (whoever they are) – and all these things take energy.

We are, too, becoming increasingly aware of the pollution of our environment that serves to sap our energy. Signs of this include the choice of lead-free petrol which is now available at filling-stations, the increasing popularity of water filters and negative ionisers in our homes. But did you know for example of the electro-magnetic pollution that invisibly assails us from a whole variety of sources: electric power lines and car radios outside our homes, microwaves, electric blankets, television sets within them? And at our place of work, computers and fluorescent lighting. If you find this hard to believe, just think of how drained you sometimes feel at the end of an evening slumped in front of the television.

Everybody's energy requirements are different, and also vary from time to time. Have you considered, for example, *why* you want to increase your energy? It may be because you are under extra pressure at work and feel you need more energy in order to be able to cope. You may be a housewife who perhaps has an outside job as well as having to shop, cook, clean the house and bring up a family – which is a full-time job anyway, especially if you happen to be a single parent. Perhaps your energy is flagging because you are under stress, emotional or otherwise. It may be that you are gearing yourself for giving a good performance in professional examinations, in an important interview, or in competitive sport. Perhaps you are ill, or convalescing after illness and are fed up with feeling so fragile, and perhaps with being in constant pain.

Whatever your reason for wanting to boost your energy it is important to try to become aware of *why* you don't have enough, or how you are leaking it and failing to replenish it. Otherwise it is rather like trying to fill with water a bucket that has holes in it. Are you, for example:

- Not eating enough of the right energy-giving foods?
- Eating too much and are therefore overweight?
- Not getting enough exercise and fresh air?
- Not sleeping well or long enough?
- Addicted to bad habits: excess of coffee, alcohol, sugar, tobacco and 'recreational' drugs?
- Under emotional strain, eg in your relationships?
- A prey to compulsive worrying?
- Allowing negativity (your own or that of others) to bring you down?

There are many more ways in which, perhaps unknowingly, we can lose energy – and many ways in which we can replenish and boost it. These will vary from individual to individual. In the chapters that follow I shall be offering a 'shopping list' of energy transformers at physical, mental and emotional levels, taken from many sources, ancient and modern, eastern and western. From these you will be able to choose which are for you and meet your special needs.

Ultimately, this book is about quality of life, and how to improve it by learning the ways of energy so that we can harness it for our needs, rather than being at the mercy of it. It's all up to you. For energy itself is neutral: like electricity, it can work for you or against you, make the morning toast – or burn the house down. You have to know how to use it. And for this, more awareness, more 'in-touchness' with your own process and changing energy-levels is needed.

We have to learn to recognise what forms of energy we are exposing ourselves to at any one time, to welcome in the nourishing ones – and to protect ourselves from the toxic. And these forms of energy can work for or against our sense of wellbeing at a very subtle, but no less real level. The living environment, for example, that we create for ourselves at home is something we need to be aware of: the lighting, the colours we choose when redecorating, the direction the head of our bed is pointing in, even the design of our furniture. Did you know for example that sharp corners and angular lines emit yang energy that can make us feel restless?

Energy, like electricity, is invisible, but none the less real. Our energy field surrounds us and extends about arms-length from our bodies. It can be photographed, using the process invented in 1939–40 by a Russian engineer named Kirlian, and his wife Valentina. The field shows up as whirls and colours – our 'aura' – which varies in brilliance and clarity depending on how well we are. Sometimes, if we are particularly relaxed and look past another person, we can see this aura. Kirlian found that one day, when he had a cold, the energy field around his hand showed up as faint and blurred while that of his wife (who was well) remained clear and bright. Since then research undertaken in Russia and (in the 1970s in the West) has shown that it is possible to use Kirlian photography to diagnose certain illnesses before the symptoms become manifest.

Our energy states are constantly changing. We can manipulate them by drinking coffee and alcohol, smoking tobacco, marijuana or taking sleeping pills. We do these things to relax or stimulate us, to get 'high' or to send ourselves off to sleep. But quite apart from what we ourselves do, our energy states also change spontaneously, and according to a definite and recurring rhythm. The founder of this theory of 'biorhythms' was a German physician Dr Wilhelm Fliess, a sometime friend of Freud before (like most of Freud's friends) they quarrelled. It is possible nowadays to have your biorhythm chart made up on a computer which has been supplied with your date of birth. From this it can be worked out which days during the next couple of months are going to be critical energywise for you. For example, on which days you are more likely to fall ill, have an accident, be emotionally unstable or intellectually below par. A professor of psychology at Southern State College in the USA, Harold Willis, found that over half of the patients who died in 1973 at a local hospital had expired on one of their 'critical' days, biorhythmically speaking. The following year a follow-up study of over 100 patients showed the same pattern.

According to the theory of biorhythms we all have a physical cycle of 23 days, an emotional cycle of 28 days, and an intellectual cycle of 33 days. The intellectual cycle affects our concentration, judgement and ability to learn. The emotional cycle affects our moods and emotions, while the physical cycle affects body coordination, stamina and resistance to illness. Each cycle when charted on a graph forms a wave-like pattern (see my own charts on page 6). On the days at the top of the wave, energy in that sphere will be high and conversely, at the bottom of the wave it will be low. In between there is a 'critical' period when the curve crosses the line. At these times our energy will be unstable, especially if the critical periods of two or all three cycles happen to coincide. The first biorhythm calculator was produced by the Swiss in 1927 and they have used them (as have the Americans and Japanese) in factories for safety, in hospitals for calculating the best days for surgery, and in the selection of national gymnastic teams for high-level performance.

Our energy, then, fluctuates naturally. It has been estimated, for example, that 30% of women will suffer every month from premenstrual tension lasting up to a week or more. Many people are affected by the full moon – and not only women. It took me some years to trace a connection between my restlessness and waking up during the early hours of the morning with energy (usually I drop off within minutes of my head touching the pillow and am a sound sleeper), and the phase of the moon. It is now quite predictable that, in the five days or so leading up to the full moon I shall experience this scattered energy, difficulty in concentrating during the day and disturbed sleep at night. It is as if I have more energy than I know how to handle. Once the moon is full, it stops. Studies carried out on 100 patients over five years at the University of Illinois established that chest pains and bleeding from ulcers were more frequent in patients around the time of a full moon.

As well as fluctuating in level, the quality of our energy also varies

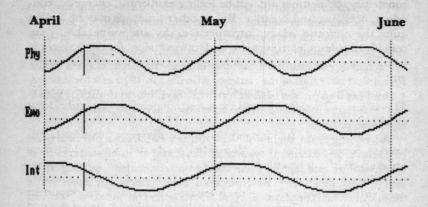

Curve plot for 65 days from Sun 1 Apr 1990 to show physical, emotional and intellectual cycles

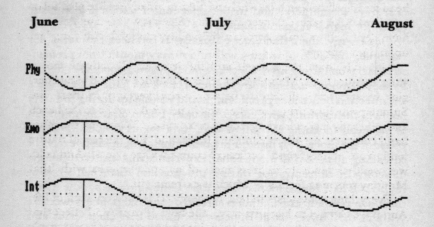

Curve plot for 65 days from Fri 1 Jun 1990 to show physical, emotional and intellectual cycles

constantly. Sometimes we will be feeling exuberant, energetic, confident, outgoing and creative. But at other times we may be feeling quite the opposite – lazy, introspective, shy and vulnerable. Jung coined the names 'extroversion' and 'introversion' for these states of being 'out' or 'in'. In eastern philosophy they are classified as yang or yin.

Sometimes one hears people talk about 'male' or 'female' energy. This is misleading, for yin and yang are independent of gender. Men can be gentle and vulnerable too (yin energy) – and woman can be tough and creative (yang energy). And at different times both will need to be either yin or yang, depending on the activity in which they are engaging. Neither type of energy is 'good' or 'bad' – it is a question of appropriateness. For example, when we are playing tennis we need to have an aggressive yang energy available if our opponent is not to wipe the floor with us. On the other hand, being flooded with this type of energy if we are meditating or trying to get to sleep is not conducive to either. Similarly, feeling very yin on a busy day at work will make your work feel draining and the day seem endless.

Yin and yang are not so much opposites as complementing each other and if we have been too much or too long in one state, the natural process is to move over to the other. For example, after engaging in strenuous sport, which is yang, most of us will either head for the clubroom bar (where we take in yin drinks like alcohol or soft drinks), or take a shower and relax. Sleep is a yin state. After we have slept well we emerge from it (hopefully) charged with yang 'get up and go' energy.

Life-style, diet, the seasons and the weather all activate yin or yang energies in us. Macrobiotics seeks to balance yin and yang energies: meat-eaters will tend to be more yang, vegetarians more yin. Summer sunshine brings out the yang in us: we travel, go to the beach and generally feel more outgoing and expansive. Winter on the other hand contracts us: we stay indoors more, and, like the rest of nature tend to go 'underground' (unless of course we are skiers). And cold, wet weather tends to depress most of us and leave us with 'that Monday morning feeling' – which is extreme yin.

Everything, physicists tell us, is energy. It is the very stuff of life. And if we can get to learn its ways, the laws of cause and effect that govern it, our lives become much easier and much more manageable (as well as more interesting). We become more empowered to be the way *we* want to be, to achieve our goals, to create consciously what we need for greater wellbeing (whether it be more zest and stamina, deeper relaxation, better health, success, more satisfying ways of relating) rather than feeling stuck with what we get.

Learning to flow with energy rather than resisting it, accepting things the way they are, rather than trying to impose our own ideas of how they should be, is a recipe for health, serenity, and harmonious relationships. If, on the other hand, we do not ride the horse the way it is going (or, to change the metaphor, try to 'push the river'), all we will end up with is disillusionment, frustration – and exhaustion.

2

FOOD FOR ENERGY

The difficulty in generalising about diet is that we are all different and have differing energy needs that are constantly varying, according to our circumstances. The diet that suits one person may be totally inappropriate for another. Older people need less energy and will therefore have less appetite than younger people. Those who engage in strenuous competitive sports will need a different diet to, say, patients recovering after serious illness. High-powered executives who want to be able to work a 12-hour day will need a different diet to those who already feel that they are under enough stress and want to slow down. The basic question is, 'what *sort* of energy do you want more of?' Do you, for example, need more physical strength, more stamina, more ability to concentrate, or simply to feel more alive and have more 'get up and go'?

The close interconnection between mind and body is very much in evidence in the effects of food on the body and digestion generally. If you feel that this or that diet is going to do you good, it will. Similarly, if you tell yourself while you are putting something in your mouth that you shouldn't be eating or drinking it, then you can be sure that you will derive little nourishment from it. I heard recently that children with leukaemia or other forms of cancer are being allowed to eat 'junk food' in certain hospitals: lots of chips, biscuits, sausages, hamburgers, all the things that we are told we shouldn't be eating. But because they enjoy them, they put on weight, which they did not with dreary, so-called 'healthy food'. It would seem that 'a little of what you fancy' does indeed do you good.

We experience energy on a feeling, intuitive level (that is, if we are sensitive enough) as 'vibrations'. For example, we say that So-and-So has 'good vibrations' if they are warm and friendly, or 'bad vibrations' if they are surly, aggressive or bad-tempered. A place, too, can be good or bad vibrationally, depending on what has happened there, or the quality of the energy of its former inhabitants, which stays around after they have left. This is why we usually feel a definite reaction, favourable or unfavourable, when we move into a new place, be it a new home or a hotel room. If people have been unhappy there, have quarrelled a lot or been unkind to each other or depressed and lonely, a sensitive person will feel a cold, scattered or depressive atmosphere on entering the space. A place with good vibrations will on the other hand immediately appeal: it will feel light, fresh and relaxing to be in. I suspect that our decision to take or reject the room/house is based more on these subliminal perceptions than on other more 'reasonable' factors like layout or expense.

All foods, like everything else, carry their own particular vibrations. As the yogis say, 'We are what we eat', and these vibrations become a part of us. If we are going for strength and stamina, then the obvious thing is to eat more meat. If we want more clarity, eating fruit and vegetables will leave us lighter and more able to concentrate. But it is all a question of *balance* and we all have to work it out for ourselves. Too much of anything is a bad thing. Meat, for example, certainly strengthens – it is high in protein (essential for energy), vitamins, minerals and amino-acids. But we have to weigh against this the fact that red meat in particular is fatty and therefore high in cholesterol. Also, when we eat meat we take into ourselves the adrenalin released by the animal's panic on the way to slaughter, or, in the case of chicken, the unhappy vibrations of a battery hen who has probably never seen the light of day (quite apart from the risk of salmonella). On the other hand, an exclusively vegetarian diet could well leave us dangerously short of vitamin B12, found only in animal foods.

This principle of a balanced diet is very much part of the system of macrobiotics developed by Georges Ohsawa. According to this 'way of food', all food carries either yin or yang energy. Optimum functioning, health and a sense of wellbeing depend very much on balancing the two. It follows that the more *living* foods we put into our bodies, the more alive we shall feel. Similarly, eating 'heavy' foods will weigh us down, make us feel sluggish and sleepy, and not in the best condition to handle that meeting or those customers, or to concentrate on the work we have in hand.

What do we mean by 'living foods'? Fresh foods that still have life in them and are unadulterated with additives such as colourings, emulsifiers, preservatives, anti-oxidants and stabilisers. Foods like fresh fruit and vegetables, nuts, seeds and pulses. These also have the advantage of being easy to digest (and therefore light) as well as providing the vitamins, minerals and fibre we need every day.

By contrast, meat is hard to digest and putrefies in the bowel. Add to this the high cholesterol fats in meat and one can readily understand why vegetarianism has become increasingly popular over the last few years.

And yet it is not that simple. Meat is the most concentrated form of protein there is, and from time to time we may need extra protein. Your need may be to put on body weight quickly, and to have more strength and stamina available, perhaps for weightlifting or other competitive sporting events you may be participating in. Or you may be convalescing after serious illness, be otherwise under stress, or needing the extra energy to cope with work pressures.

If we are taking in too many yang foods we will tend to be restless, unable to relax and perhaps sleep, over-reactive, almost as if we have more energy than we know what to do with. On the other hand, too much yin in our diet will manifest itself in a lack of energy, listlessness, even depression.

Macrobiotics is an attempt to return to a more natural diet. The most natural staple diet for human beings is whole grains (eg brown rice) and vegetables. This is based on the proportion of molar to incisor teeth. We are not, it is claimed, flesh-eaters by nature. This is certainly a diet you could try for a while if you feel the state of your energy is not as you would like it to be. I was put on it a few years ago for six months by a Japanese dietician. He decided that I was too yang and that an exclusive diet of rice and vegetables would balance my energy. It was boring – but it worked, and from time to time I go back to it.

But no food is barred *per se* in macrobiotics. We should eat according to our energy levels and needs, and also the climate we live in. Thus in winter (yin) we need the body heat supplied by meat (yang). On the other hand, in summer (yang) we naturally feel drawn to cooling salads and drinks (yin). There is a natural tendency for our bodies to want to balance our energy and if we are sensitive to them we will feel naturally drawn to the sorts of foods we need. Unfortunately, most of us have lost this natural intuition as to what we need. We can become addicted to things that are positively bad for us, sugar, for example, junk foods and alcohol. It is probably true, however, that our attitude to what we eat is just as important as *what* we eat. As I said earlier, 'A little of what you fancy does you good' – and if you think something is going to do you harm (or feel guilty about eating it) it probably will.

If you find yourself lacking in energy you should ask yourself the following questions. Am I:

- Missing or skimping on meals?
- Eating too much?
- Getting enough protein?
- Getting enough vitamins and minerals?
- Taking too much sugar?
- Getting enough fibre?
- Drinking enough during the day?
- Drinking too much alcohol?
- Not allowing myself to digest food properly?

UNDER-EATING

Don't expect to be brimming over with energy if you are not supplying your body-machine with enough fuel, and fuel of the right kind. (We shall be discussing what we mean by 'the right kind' later.) It may be that you have lost your appetite because you have been ill, are suffering from depression or are in a crisis situation. Or it may be that you are so busy rushing around that you don't give yourself time for refuelling. Perhaps, by the end of a gruelling day you just can't be bothered to cook a decent meal for yourself and send out for a pizza. One of the things that people who are living alone have to watch is the feeling that there is not much point in preparing a nice dinner if you don't have someone to share it with. You can get away with this over a short period of time, but sooner or later it will begin to take its toll on your energy. You do deserve good food whether you have someone to share it with or not and choosing to nourish yourself properly is in fact a statement of your self-worth, as well as an investment in your wellbeing.

Preparing a decent meal doesn't *have* to be time-consuming. Avocados, for example, are immensely nourishing – and all you have to do is cut them in half and add a dressing. Soups too are nutritious, and will cook themselves whilst you are in the bath. Eggs, cheese, bread (wholewheat), salads, fruit and yoghurts take no time at all to prepare and will keep you supplied with the necessary vitamins and minerals.

OVER-EATING

It is more likely, though, that you may be eating too much. Unless you have a job that is physically demanding it is easy to meet your calorie requirements (2500–3000 per day for the average man, 1750–2250 for the average woman). Excess calories, unless burnt up in exercise, will make you overweight, which apparently is the case with 35% of the population. Increasing your energy, for you, may therefore mean that you have to lose weight. As well as putting strain on the heart and other internal organs and predisposing us to varicose veins and back trouble, being overweight saps our energy simply because there is more of us to drag around. Not only that, but we don't *look* so good either – and when we know we *look* good most of us tend to *feel* good.

So monitor your weight on the bathroom scales when you remember – and try not to get obsessive about it. The charts on pages 14 and 15 will give you some idea of your optimum weight for your size. If you want to have more energy you may have to lose a few kilos.

How to lose weight is a perennial source of fascination to women's and health magazines. One can become quite confused with the 'wonder' diets being urged on us from all sides, especially as they often contradict each other. There are, however, certain things you have to bear in mind once you have decided to lose weight.

1 Don't try to go too fast. If you do, and deprive yourself of essential proteins, vitamins and minerals you will end up with less rather than more energy – and possibly ill as well.
2 Eat little and often, rather than heavy meals.
3 Take more exercise (see the next chapter).
4 Drinking a few glasses of water before you eat will make you want to eat less.
5 Always leave the table feeling that you could have eaten more.

The difficulty many people have in sticking to diets is often due to patterns in their subconscious which sabotage their best intentions. The battle, however, is often half-won if one can become aware of just why one is a compulsive eater and exactly what food has come to symbolise.

Some years ago a client came to me for counselling. Her presenting problem was that she felt unattractive and wondered why she had never had a relationship with a man. She was in her forties, very

YOUR IDEAL WEIGHT
(in kilos)

MEN

HEIGHT (in cm)	SMALL BONED	AVERAGE	BIG BONED
160	55.7	59.2	63.7
162	57.2	60.7	65.2
164	58.7	62.2	66.7
166	60.1	63.6	66.1
168	61.6	65.1	69.6
170	63.1	66.6	71.1
172	64.6	68.1	72.6
174	66.1	69.6	74.1
176	67.5	71.0	75.5
178	69.0	72.5	77.0
180	70.5	74.0	78.5
182	72.0	75.5	80.0
184	73.5	77.0	81.5
186	74.9	78.4	82.9
188	76.4	79.9	84.4
190	77.9	81.4	85.9

WOMEN

HEIGHT (in cm)	SMALL BONED	AVERAGE	BIG BONED
150	47.0	50.5	54.0
152	48.2	51.7	55.2
154	49.5	53.0	56.5
156	50.7	54.2	57.7
158	52.0	55.5	59.0
160	53.2	56.7	60.2
162	54.4	57.9	61.4
164	55.7	59.2	62.7
166	56.9	60.4	63.9
168	58.2	61.7	65.2
170	59.4	62.9	66.4
172	60.6	64.1	67.6
174	61.9	65.4	68.9
176	63.1	66.6	70.1
178	64.4	67.9	71.4
180	65.6	69.1	72.6

CHECK YOUR WEIGHT
(in stones and pounds)

MEN

HEIGHT (in feet and inches)	IDEAL	ACCEPTABLE	OBESE
5.2	8.9	8.0 – 10.1	12.1
5.3	9.1	8.3 – 10.4	12.5
5.4	9.4	8.6 – 10.8	12.10
5.5	9.7	8.9 – 10.12	13.0
5.6	9.10	8.12 – 11.2	13.5
5.7	10.0	9.2 – 11.7	13.11
5.8	10.5	9.6 – 11.12	14.3
5.9	10.9	9.10 – 12.2	14.8
5.10	10.13	10.0 – 12.6	14.13
5.11	11.4	10.4 – 12.11	15.5
6.0	11.8	10.8 – 13.2	15.11
6.1	11.12	10.12 – 13.7	16.3
6.2	12.3	11.2 – 13.12	16.9
6.3	12.8	11.6 – 14.3	17.1
6.4	12.13	11.10 – 14.8	17.7

WOMEN

4.10	7.4	6.8 – 8.7	10.3
4.11	7.6	6.10 – 8.10	10.6
5.0	7.9	6.12 – 8.13	10.10
5.1	7.12	7.1 – 9.2	10.13
5.2	8.1	7.4 – 9.5	11.3
5.3	8.4	7.7 – 9.8	11.7
5.4	8.8	7.10 – 9.12	11.12
5.5	8.11	7.13 – 10.2	12.2
5.6	9.2	8.2 – 10.6	12.7
5.7	9.6	8.6 – 10.10	12.12
5.8	9.10	8.10 – 11.0	13.3
5.9	10.0	9.0 – 11.4	13.8
5.10	10.4	9.4 – 11.9	14.0
5.11	10.8	9.8 – 12.0	14.6
6.0	10.12	9.12 – 12.5	14.12

From *Obesity:* a Report by the Royal College of Physicians.

lonely, and with (as is often the case) a low self-image. During one session she happened to mention that she would like to lose weight, but had tried different diets without success. She would lose weight, but always seemed to put it on again. It was only after several more sessions that it emerged that keeping herself overweight was an expression of her basic attitudes, of which she was only dimly conscious. Getting involved with a man terrified her. Her idea of what marriage entailed was based on that of her parents. Her mother had become a drudge, had told her often that sex was no fun and was something 'to put up with'. Perhaps not surprisingly, her husband had left her, leaving her very bitter.

Also hardly surprisingly, at some unconscious level, my client had come to equate relationships with loss of independence and freedom. It would have been very hard for her to be an equal partner in a relationship because of her own lack of sense of her own value. So, to protect herself from becoming a doormat like her mother she chose instead (albeit unconsciously) to make herself unattractive to men by becoming overweight. There was more to it than that, of course. There always is – like not wanting to be considered a 'fast woman' by making herself attractive, not wanting to be disloyal to her mother by wanting to get close to the 'enemy' (men) and so on.

Very often, food can be a substitute for love. Another client of mine who was overweight could not understand why she could not stop raiding the fridge at night even though she didn't feel hungry, and perhaps had been out to a very good dinner. Her pattern was that she was a compulsive giver, both in her job (she was a beautician) and with her friends. For some years she had been having a relationship with a married man and able to see him only when he was in London on a business trip. The satisfaction she derived from this liaison was becoming increasingly threadbare. She felt that she could not ask more from him in the sense of a deeper relationship than he was in a position to give, and increasingly felt the desire for a child of her own as she got older. But, since she loved him, she felt unable to end the relationship. Her compulsive eating was an attempt to fill this continual sense of dissatisfaction and emptiness.

This association of food and love is very common and dates back to our earliest experience of love and nurturing at our mother's breast. (It also applies to those who felt they never had enough of this nurturing.) This may not be your problem. Other unconscious motivations for making oneself fat that I have come across are the subconscious wish to make oneself physically bigger to compensate for feelings of inferiority and inadequacy, or to protect one's vital organs if one is too vulnerable. The point is to become aware (either through introspection or counselling) of what subconscious patterns are sabotaging your conscious intention to lose weight. Unless you do so, you could diet till kingdom come without losing a kilo – or lose it, and promptly put on weight again.

If you want to lose weight the foods to avoid are sugar (and foods that contain a lot of sugar) and fried foods. Sugar contains no nutrients whatsoever – which makes it the 'junkiest' of junk foods. It is almost unavoidable, for it is added to a wide range of items like soft drinks, packet soups and pickles. It is not surprising that most people are getting nearly a quarter of their calorie intake from sugar alone. The average person's intake of sugar is estimated at 110lbs per year. Fifty per cent of this intake is accounted for by taking it in tea or coffee. And if you take a slice of chocolate cake with it, that is the equivalent of 10½ teaspoons of sugar . . .

Quite apart from the harmful effects on health which include obesity, tooth decay, greater risk of diabetes and coronary heart disease, sugar does not in fact increase our energy, except temporarily. It is paradoxical that, even though sugar is an extremely concentrated form of energy, taking too much of it actually *lowers* our energy level. We tend to become drowsy and irritable, and find it hard to concentrate. This is because the body responds to the sudden influx of sugar into the bloodstream by producing insulin, which lowers the blood sugar level too much. These effects are felt quickly, because when we are inactive our brains are using quite a high proportion of our total energy consumption (about 500 calories a day).

Fried foods, too, should be avoided. Not only does the high fat content make us put on weight and clog our arteries, but it is also hard to digest.

PROTEIN

Adequate protein intake is essential for 'get up and go' energy. Proteins are the building blocks of the body, and the stuff from which all our cells are made. We need protein, not only for repairing wear and tear, but also for energy. If you are not getting enough the effects will show in fatigue, irritability and inability to concentrate. Unless you are low on energy due to anaemia, or going through a particularly stressful time (in which case you could do with vitamin B12 found in meat, especially liver), it is healthier to get your protein from other sources. The main foods, apart from meat, that are rich in protein are:

- fish
- eggs
- milk
- cheese
- nuts
- wholemeal bread
- pulses (eg beans and lentils)
- fruit and vegetables.

You might also like to try tofu, made from soya beans, one of the richest forms of protein there is. (Soya beans also have the advantage of being very inexpensive.)

VITAMINS

We shall be short on energy if we neglect to make sure we are getting enough vitamins, especially vitamin B. The following list will give you some idea of how the body uses them, which foods contain them, and the signs of deficiency.

Vitamin B

The most complex of all the vitamins. B vitamins are particularly important for our purposes because most of them are concerned with the ability of the body to convert the food we eat into energy. They are also essential for maintaining the nervous system. Deficiency of folic acid and B12 could also cause severe anaemia, for they are needed for the production of red blood cells.

B1 (thiamin)

Essential for growth, health of muscles and nerves and the conversion of carbohydrates into energy.

Signs of Deficiency: fatigue, irritability, depression, loss of appetite, poor digestion. Very commonly also, dark shadows under the eyes.

Natural sources: meat, fish, beans, nuts, seafood, whole grains, pulses, potatoes, wheatgerm, yeast.

B2 (riboflavin)

Extracts energy from proteins and carbohydrates. Essential for growth, health of skin, eyes and red blood cells, and for general wellbeing.

Signs of Deficiency: lack of stamina, nervousness, dry hair and skin.

Natural Sources: meat, soya beans, eggs, vegetables, poultry, milk, cheese, yeast, vegetables.

B3 (niacin)

Essential for growth, digestion of carbohydrates and health of the nervous system and skin.

Signs of Deficiency: headaches, insomnia, irritability.

Natural Sources: lean meat, fish, whole grains, poultry, nuts, potatoes, dried fruit.

B6 (pyridoxine)

Essential for the body's use of protein and the health of the nerves, skin and muscles. Helps to maintain good circulation and to prevent heart disease. Boosts the immune system. Has been found useful in treating premenstrual tension.

Signs of Deficiency: irritability, shakiness, insomnia, depression, anxiety.

Natural Sources: meat, fish, poultry, whole grains, green vegetables, milk, fruit (especially bananas).

Folic Acid

Essential for growth, healthy blood and fertility.

Signs of Deficiency: anaemia, weakness, fatigue, depression.

Natural Sources: spinach, endive, brussel sprouts, broccoli, potatoes, wholewheat flour, lentils.

Biotin

Needed for healthy nerves, skin and muscles.

Signs of Deficiency: hair loss, eczema.

Natural Sources: liver, kidneys, eggs, nuts, wheatgerm.

B5 (pantothenic acid)

Converts energy from proteins, fats and carbohydrates.

Signs of Deficiency: dry skin and hair.

Natural Sources: most foods contain it.

B12 (cyanocobalamin)

Essential for the body's conversion of protein and for the health of nerves, blood and skin.

Signs of Deficiency: fatigue, anaemia.

Natural Sources: liver, poultry, lean meat, eggs, yeast, milk, cheese. Not found in vegetables. Vegans therefore need to take B12 supplements.

Since the B vitamins are water-soluble and cannot be stored in the body, we have to ensure that we get enough of them every day. It is important to take the whole complex rather than just one or two of them. Two or three tablets of Brewer's Yeast a day supplies all the B vitamins except B12.

I have not given the RDAs (Recommended Daily Allowances) because these are now out of date. They were set up as minimum dietary requirements for mass feeding programmes during the Second World War when food was rationed. Any excess of vitamin B will be passed out in your urine, so if your urine is bright yellow you know you've taken more vitamin B than you need.

The other vitamins are not as crucial as vitamin B for supplying energy, but they are nevertheless essential for maintaining us in good health. Vitamin C is particularly important for maintaining resistance to disease, and speeding recovery from illness. It is mostly found in fresh fruit (especially citrus fruits, strawberries and rosehips) and in vegetables (especially leafy, green ones). Take vitamin C every day, and lots of it if you feel you are coming down with a cold or the 'flu, or are convalescing after surgery, for it promotes healing. Mega doses of vitamin C are being used in the treatment of AIDS and cancer. The more ill you are, the more you need to take. When your limit has been reached (shown by the onset of diarrhoea), the dose should be cut by 25%.

With vitamin A one has to be careful not to take too much as this could be toxic. In the form of beta-carotene, vitamin A is particularly good for the immune system. A glass or two of freshly-made carrot juice (mixed with a little oil to aid absorption) is a delicious way to get your vitamin A. The richest sources of this vitamin are liver, leafy, green vegetables (eg spinach, parsley, cabbage, lettuce), carrots and red or yellow fruits (eg apricots, melons, oranges).

In winter when we are short of sunshine it could be a good idea to take halibut or cod liver oil capsules, which as well as vitamin A are rich in vitamin D. Other natural sources of vitamin D are sardines, salmon, herrings, eggs, butter, margarine – and of course, sunshine.

Try to remember to take vitamin E daily. It has a cleansing effect on the body, counteracts the effects of stress and pollution, and has a rejuvenating effect. It is also claimed that vitamin E is good for your sex life. Like vitamin C, it is an anti-oxidant and scavenger of free radicals – molecular fragments capable of damaging cells, causing genetic damage and even causing cancer.

Natural sources of this vitamin are leafy, green vegetables, eggs, whole grain cereals, wheatgerm, seeds (eg sunflower), nuts and cold-pressed vegetable oils.

Take extra vitamins if you are:

● Ill or convalescent.
● A heavy smoker or drinker: each cigarette leeches 25mg from our store of vitamin C, while heavy drinking also depletes us of vitamin B.
● Slimming.
● Using contraceptive pills.
● Pregnant or breastfeeding.
● Suffer from premenstrual tension (especially B6).
● Are on antibiotics (in which case also take acidophilus to restore beneficent flora to the intestines).

MINERALS

If you are low on energy this could be due to mineral rather than vitamin deficiency. Minerals can not be manufactured in the body. They are present in the soil as inorganic elements and are absorbed by plants, which are then eaten by animals. Thus, we get our supply of minerals from plant and animal foods.

Our bodies need more than 15 different minerals for health, growth and energy, and deficiency in some of these can result in fatigue, depression, emotional tension or anaemia. The minerals you are most likely to be deficient in are iron and calcium. The others (eg phosphorus, magnesium, sodium, potassium and sulphur) are so widely found in foods that deficiencies are rare. Magnesium deficiency can, however, be caused by drinking too much alcohol.

Iron

Iron deficiency anaemia has been recognised by the Department of Health as being very common, especially among women. When this occurs, cells are starved of oxygen, causing one to feel tired, irritable or depressed. Women who have very heavy blood loss during menstruation may need to take iron supplements to compensate. Foods rich in iron are meat, liver, kidneys, wholegrain cereals (muesli and Weetabix are particularly rich), spinach, lentils, dried apricots, prunes and peanut butter. Note that one should not take iron supplements if one has a bacterial infection, for iron can actually *feed* the bacteria. Check with your doctor.

Calcium

A deficiency of calcium disturbs the function of muscles and nerve cells, with the result that we may be excitable, unable to relax or sleep properly. Calcium is found in dairy products, fish, vegetables, and eggs. Calcium pantothenate is particularly useful for counteracting the effects of stress when we are going through a bad time. A combination of liver, leafy, green vegetables, wheatgerm, milk and calcium pantothenate makes the ideal anti-stress diet – plus, of course, extra B and C vitamins.

Zinc and Selenium

These are essential for good immunity. Zinc is found in seafood, liver, mushrooms, soya beans, spinach and sunflower seeds. It is lost through alcohol abuse and (for men) over-indulgence in sex to the point of orgasm. So, gentlemen, if your sex life is getting hectic make sure you include the above foods in your diet – or take 15mg of zinc as a supplement.

Selenium was shown by research done in 1984 to be the most potent anti-carcinogen there is. But be careful not to take too much of it, as it can be highly toxic if taken to excess. Selenium is found in fish, whole grains, cereals and wholewheat bread, milk, butter, garlic, fruit and nuts.

THE ENERGY DIET

Whether or not we choose to include meat in our daily diet, it should now be obvious what our staple diet should be if we want to stay healthy and maintain a high energy level. It should include:

- Fish (oily fish is particularly good for you, eg sardines, herring).
- Freshly-made soups.
- Poultry (but make sure it is well cooked).
- Eggs (sparingly – a couple of times a week, and always free range).
- Vegetables (especially leafy, green ones – and a lot of them).
- Salads.
- Whole grains (eg brown rice, bulgar, wholewheat bread).
- Fruit.
- Pulses.
- Nuts and seeds.
- Soya products (eg tofu, miso paste in soups, tamari).
- Vegetable oils (the best are olive oil and grape seed oil).

Eat dairy products sparingly, and not at all if you have a cold, for they produce mucus. Also, use a lot of garlic. It is a powerful antibiotic, cleanses the blood, is good both for the immune and the digestive systems. The smell of the garlic can be dispelled by chewing fresh parsley. If you prefer, you can take garlic oil capsules instead.

FOOD PREPARATION

Vitamins and minerals can be lost in the process of cooking, especially B and C which are soluble in water. When you cook vegetables:

- **Steam them rather than boil.**
  Handy for this are the Chinese-style wooden steamers that you can set over a saucepan of boiling water, containing, for example, potatoes. Otherwise use very little water (none at all for spinach, except the water that clings to it after washing) and save the residue of the water for stocks (or drink it), for it will be rich in nutrients.

- **Fry as little as possible, unless you stir-fry.**
  Invest in a wok and use only as much oil as is needed to keep the food from burning. Fast stir-frying seals in the vitamins. If you wish, you could add a little water, but do not cover the wok or the vegetables will come out mushy. Use miso (soya paste) or tamari (soya sauce) to flavour rather than salt, which doesn't do your arteries any good.

- **Scrape vegetables rather than peel them.**
  Much of the goodness, for example in carrots, lies just below the skin. If the vegetables are not too dirty you can simply brush them clean with a vegetable brush available in most supermarkets.

- **Do not leave washed, peeled vegetables lying around for any length of time.**
  Vitamin C can be destroyed when cut surfaces of food are left exposed to air. Prepare vegetables just before you start cooking.

Do not sit down to eat if you feel wound up or upset in any way, for this does not make for good digestion. If you have just got in from work, give yourself time to relax before you eat. Our digestive system starts in our mouths, so don't bolt your food. Come away from the table feeling satisfied but not bloated. Energy naturally goes down to the stomach after we've eaten – so don't do anything too energetic then. Don't eat a heavy meal shortly before retiring for the night – it doesn't make for sound sleep.

Remember that food is energy, and can pick it up from outside. So never cook if you are irritated or otherwise disturbed. Don't attempt to prepare the evening meal in the middle of a flaming row with your partner. Even if you don't burn everything it will be quite tasteless – and you won't enjoy it anyway if you are both sulking. And don't allow anyone else to cook for you if they have 'bad vibes'. On one or two occasions I have left a restaurant without ordering if the waiter is rude or dismissive. Yes, it is a hard job, and he may have had a hard day. But why should I give myself indigestion?

FIBRE

One of the things that can cause sluggish, low energy, as well as constipation and headaches, is not eating enough fibre. But if you include plenty of vegetables, pasta, rice and bread in your daily diet this should be sufficient. If, however, you are constipated, avoid laxatives and breakfast instead on stewed fruit, especially prunes, and acidophilus.

While we are on the subject of breakfast it should be said that for many dieticians it is the most important meal of the day, in which we 'break our fast' after our longest spell without food. To do without breakfast before going off to work, as many do, and to keep your energy up by drinking cups of coffee is not a good idea, especially in winter when we need fuel to maintain our body heat and blood sugar levels.

And breakfast does not *have* to be eggs and bacon. You could ring the changes on muesli with fruit, nuts and sunflower seeds, fruit, or porridge and toasted wholewheat bread.

DRINKS

Ideally, one should not drink whilst eating, as this dilutes digestive juices. But this is often hard to do, especially if you are having a celebration dinner with friends. But if you are eating alone, try to save your liquid intake until after your meal.

It is important to drink enough, especially in hot weather. We can easily get dehydrated without being aware of it, with resulting weakness, lassitude and breathlessness. Between two and three litres per day is the required amount. This is needed to replace the moisture we lose in the course of the day, which is:

	ml per day
sweating	600
exhaling	400
defecation	100
urine	1550

Cut down on . . .

Alcohol

We usually think of alcohol as a stimulant and often fix ourselves a drink 'to give us a lift'. But in fact it is really a depressant, and depresses all the cells in our body. Its relaxing effect comes from the fact that it lessens brain activity and thus deadens anxiety. Really, alcohol is only fermented sugar, which, as we have seen, is not good for you. It is bad for the liver and leeches precious vitamins, especially vitamin B6, an essential nutrient of the immune system. In fact, for the last 60 years alcohol has been associated with increased risk of cancer.

Curiously enough, though, treating oneself to one or two glasses of wine per day has actually been shown to protect against coronary heart disease, and surveys have also shown that those who indulge in small amounts of alcohol tend to live longer than teetotallers. So the odd drink won't do you any harm. Also the pleasure derived from the odd glass or two with dinner will counteract the toxicity. What has to be avoided is going on a binge or habitual drinking, especially of spirits, and especially if you are on drugs of any kind. The BMA (British Medical Association) suggests that a safe level of alcohol intake is up to 24 units of alcohol per week for men and 14 for women. A unit of alcohol is equivalent to one glass of wine, one measure of spirits or half a pint of beer.

Caffeine

Caffeine is found not only in coffee, but also in tea, cocoa and cola drinks. The 'buzz' we get from these drinks is due to the adrenalin-like stimulation of the nervous system and the heart, and the dilation of blood vessels.

Caffeine has been suspected of contributing to cancer (especially of the pancreas, the fourth most common cause of cancer deaths). Just drinking small amounts of coffee increases by ten times the formation in the stomach of nitrosamines, some of which are known to be carcinogens. Drinking hot beverages out of plastic or polystyrene cups also increases the risk. If you really must have your coffee, keep it down to a maximum of three cups per day. And do not drink coffee if you are taking homoeopathic remedies, for the effect will be to cancel out the remedy for up to 60 days afterwards. Rather than being addicted to coffee, use it to sharpen you up on those occasions when you need to be particularly wide awake, eg before a business meeting. Tea is not so drastic and you would have to drink 20 cups of it to match the stimulating effect of just one cup of coffee. It is even more delicious with a wedge of lemon, and, if you like it sweet, with a teaspoon or two of honey.

Soft drinks

Avoid these since most of them contain a lot of sugar or artificial sweeteners. Too many of them and you will very likely experience 'sugar blues'. The body responds to a sudden influx of sugar into the bloodstream by producing insulin, which lowers the blood sugar level too much. Since the brain can only use blood sugars as fuel, it starts running in low gear. The result is drowsiness, irritability and difficulty in concentration. These effects are felt rapidly because when we are inactive the brain is using quite a high percentage of our total energy consumption (about 500 calories a day).

Drink more

Water

Assuming your water supply is relatively pure, you can't drink enough of it. Drink a large glass of water first thing in the morning. Once again, squeezing fresh lemon juice into it makes it more interesting. (The addition of lemon, incidentally, is considered to balance your energy.) It is a good idea to buy a water filter to purify your water. Make sure you drink regularly throughout the day, especially in hot weather and that you make up your two to three litres. Keep a jug of iced, purified water in your fridge, so that every time you open it you are reminded that you have to drink plenty.

Fresh fruit and vegetable juices

It is an investment in your health to buy a machine that can produce fresh juices. Carrot and/or beet juice are particularly good as, being high in beta-carotene, they are very beneficial for your immune system. Go easy on the citrus fruit drinks, however, as they are very acid and our blood should be slightly alkaline.

Herb teas

These may not give you the stimulation you have been used to getting from tea or coffee, but when you get used to them they can be quite delicious – and are certainly better for you. Ring the changes with mint, camomile, lime, rosehip (specially rich in vitamin C). Sweeten with acacia honey if you wish.

CLEANSING DIETS

Your energy will certainly get a boost if you go on a cleansing diet or fast for a day or so. You will feel lighter and clearer, especially if you have been eating too much of the wrong foods. Drinking a glass of warm water first thing in the morning with a teaspoon of cider vinegar in it makes a good start to the day, and is especially good for clearing mucus from the digestive system. Here are some other ideas you may like to try:

● **Raw foods.**
These can be quite delicious, especially in summer. As well as preserving all the nutrients (because they are not lost in the cooking process) they provide a lot of fibre.

Virtually any vegetable is suitable for inclusion in a raw food meal. Ring the changes on:
white or Chinese cabbage
lettuce
carrot
raw beet
celery
celeriac
green, yellow or red pepper
tomato
sprouting seeds
onions.

Grate the root vegetables, and cut the others into slivers. Use an olive oil and cider vinegar or fresh lemon dressing rather than mayonnaise or salad cream.

An exclusively raw food diet (as opposed to raw foods that you include in your everyday eating) is best not embarked upon when the weather is cold, as in winter. They are yin, and will not supply the protein necessary for maintaining your body heat. Also, do not go on these diets if you are under stress, pregnant, breastfeeding, anaemic, convalescing or having to cope with an extra work load.

● **Grape fast.**
Eat about a kilo of washed grapes during the day, including the pips – and drink a lot.

● **Fruit and fruit juices.**
Eat and drink as much of fruit as you want, but don't overdo the juices.

- **Brown rice.**
  This is a favourite in macrobiotics. The bad publicity it got some years ago was because people went on too long with it. A few days (maximum) should be enough to clear you out. Flavour the rice with tamari and sesame seeds. And, once again, drink a lot of water.

It is essential if you are on a cleansing diet not only to take in adequate fluids, but also vitamins, especially B and C. Also, these diets should not last more than a few days. One could also fast completely for a day (except for water), but not if you are engaged in demanding work. Again, do not go on one of these diets if you are pregnant, breastfeeding, anaemic or ill in any way.

Don't be alarmed if you experience dizziness or come out in spots while on a cleansing diet. This simply means that your body is clearing out toxins and it is a good sign. You will have much more energy when it's all over.

PICK-ME-UPS

Ginseng

This interesting root has enjoyed recognition as a medicinal plant for over 4000 years in the Far East, where it is called 'the root of life'. Chinese doctors still prescribe it today for loss of vigour (including sexual potency), anaemia, nervous disorders and insomnia. It is such a potent energy-giver that it should not be taken late in the day as it could stop you sleeping.

The Russians give ginseng to their astronauts on space missions in order to heighten their alertness, energy and endurance. Ginseng grows only in a few dry and mountainous regions in the world and takes six to seven years before it reaches maturity and the root can be harvested – which makes it a little expensive. But it is such an energy-booster, so rich in nutrients, minerals and trace elements that it is worth the cost. Choose the Siberian or Korean varieties. It is marketed in various forms: the root itself, as tea, or in vitamin-like capsules of varying potency.

A word of warning: ginseng stimulates the male hormones, so it should be taken by women sparingly and only for a few days at a time – and not at all by pregnant women.

Royal Jelly

Royal jelly is the food supplied by the worker bees to their queen, taken from bee larvae. It provides her with an amazing amount of energy and stamina and it enables her to produce eggs exceeding her own bodyweight by 2000 times – up to 3000 in 24 hours. She also lives longer than workers – five years as opposed to their six months.

Much research has been done on royal jelly, notably in the USA, USSR, France, Italy, Hungary and Belgium, as to why it is such a powerful energiser. It contains protein, B vitamins, amino-acids and enzymes. But we do not yet know exactly what about 3% of it is composed of, and this 'mystery' ingredient may in fact be what makes it so potent.

Royal jelly takes a long time to harvest, and is therefore expensive. But investing in a two months' supply could be an investment in yourself, for as well as giving you more energy, vitality and stamina, it boosts the immune system and has a good effect on hair, skin and nails. It is mixed by the manufacturers with Australian honey, yellow beeswax, wheatgerm oil, lecithin and natural vitamin E. Japanese researchers have found that royal jelly is good for people with poor appetite and sleeping problems, and older people who take it recover their zest for life.

As a leading manufacturer puts in their advertising: 'Take 200gms of royal jelly a day and you'll be flying!'

Protein Drinks

These come in various flavours and can be bought in health food stores. They are particularly suitable for invalids or those who need to put on weight, but have very little appetite. Less palatable is protein powder. However, this can be mixed with other ingredients to make a nourishing and tasty drink as follows:

● Stir 1½ tbsps of protein powder into a glass of milk. Add 1 tbsp of wheatgerm and 1 tbsp of lecithin. Flavour with honey and a fruit of your choice. Mix in a blender, chill and enjoy.

Zabaglione

This is an Italian concoction sometimes served in good restaurants as a dessert. It consists of a half glass of Marsala (a fortified wine from

Sicily) into which sugar and the yolk of an egg have been stirred. Nowadays, however, it is inadvisable to eat raw eggs because of the risk of salmonella. So bake it in a low oven, checking regularly to see that it doesn't burn or become a sticky mess. It's delicious.

ALLERGIES

Finally, a word about allergies. Signs that you may have a food allergy include skin problems (eg itching or rashes), streaming eyes, runny nose, asthma, nausea, hyperactivity, fatigue, backache, headache and depression.

An allergy is a disorder in which the body's homeostatic system goes into action as if to repel hostile invaders – which the allergens are not. The best-known allergen is pollen which causes hay fever, but one can become allergic to virtually anything, like cats, for example. Among the foods that most commonly can become allergens are milk and other dairy produce, wheat/gluten, seafood, tomatoes, but there are many others.

There is very little that can be done about allergies beyond finding out what one is allergic to – and avoiding it. One can have a blood sample tested for reaction to a whole array of potential allergens, or these can be pricked into the skin of the arm and reactions noted. If one is particularly vigilant it is possible to establish by oneself what one is allergic to. But probably the most convenient thing to do is to consult a kinesiologist who will be able to pinpoint exactly what it is you are allergic to. This is done by testing muscle strength each time a possible allergen is placed on the navel. If you are allergic to the substance, this will immediately register in weakness of, say, the arm muscles. It will be impossible to push with any strength against the hand of the kinesiologist, as compared with the normal resistance established before exposure to the allergen. The effect of avoiding these allergens will be greater energy, more clarity and a sense of wellbeing.

SUMMARY: EATING FOR ENERGY

Here is a checklist of the foods we have discussed in this chapter, to help you plan nourishing, high-energy meals. The suggested meals for lunch and dinner are interchangeable.

- **Breakfast**
  muesli with fruit, nuts and sunflower seeds
  porridge
  toasted wholewheat bread with honey
  eggs (sparingly, boiled, and free range)

- **Lunch or Dinner**
  fish
  chicken (well-cooked)
  fillet steak (grilled, occasionally when you need a lot of energy)
  liver
  vegetables (lots, preferably green, leafy ones, steamed or stir-fried, not boiled)
  potatoes (baked or boiled)
  pasta (eg vegetarian lasagne)
  whole grains (eg brown rice, bulgar, wholewheat bread)
  raw foods
  salads
  avocado
  Brussels sprouts
  fruit (fresh or stewed)
  olive oil
  garlic (lots of it)

Remember:
- Drink two to three litres of water per day.
- Aim to avoid sugar and only have small amounts of caffeine and salt.

3

CENTRING AND GROUNDING

One of the quickest ways to raise your energy is to move your body. Staying in one position for too long (whether in a sedentary occupation, a hospital bed, or simply watching television) deadens your body and stops energy flowing. The problem is compounded if at the same time you are concentrating or worrying about something. Energy gets stuck in the head, which is experienced as strain, restlessness and perhaps irritability. Having yet another cup of coffee, after the initial 'buzz', will only make you feel worse. The adrenalin will simply make you more scattered and 'speedy'.

Quite apart from relieving the tension in muscles kept too long in the same position, moving the body reminds us that we have one. We are where our attention is. For much of the day we cut ourselves off from experiencing body sensations because of the demands of our work and become just 'talking heads'. To recover body awareness comes as something of a relief and we try to do it naturally after long bouts of concentration when, for example we stand up and stretch, or rub our hands together, or massage our neck. The less in touch with your body you are, the deader you feel and, conversely, the more 'in your body' you are, the more alive.

Posture, too, is important. Change your posture and you change your mood. The more strained or nervous you feel, the more you will tend to close up your body posture (albeit unconsciously) by folding your arms and crossing your legs. This cuts down energy flow, and the longer you stay 'locked' in this position, the more strained and nervous you will feel. Opening up your posture will restore energy flow, experienced subjectively as relaxing. Similarly, people suffering from acute depression never look up, always down. Encouraging them to look up has been found to have positive therapeutic effects.

The whole of the Alexander Technique (see p 100) is based on this close connection between not only posture and mood, but also posture and physical health.

How we breathe, too, is closely connected with how we are feeling. When we are relaxed or asleep, for example, our breathing gets deeper and slower. On the other hand, when we are frightened, it becomes fast and shallow. If we are shocked we may suspend our breathing entirely. The less deeply we breathe, the less we feel. This is why a therapist will very often tell a client 'Breathe!' to encourage the flow of feelings. Much of bioenergetics, for example, is to do with facilitating catharsis and body awareness through breathing exercises (see p 100). Once again, our bodies naturally try to bring us back to equilibrium when we have been stagnating too long by making us yawn. More oxygen to the muscles means more energy, more aliveness.

This is why it is so important to take regular exercise if you want to increase your energy and feel more alive. When you exercise you breathe more fully and supply combustion fuel to your muscles. Physical activity improves circulation, strengthens the heart, removes toxins – which is why you feel better for it. Exactly how you choose to take exercise is a matter of preference. It helps, like with so many other things, if you *enjoy* it. But, to be effective, it should force you to breathe more efficiently, make your heart pump faster, increase your body awareness and, preferably, make you sweat.

To ensure the regularity of your exercising it could be a good idea to sign up at a fitness club, for you will want to make sure you are getting your money's worth – a couple of sessions a week would seem to be reasonable for most active people. If you find working out with weights, on a trampoline, or physical jerks boring, you may well prefer to play tennis, squash or badminton.

Running or jogging in the park is very popular with many. Doing it early in the morning will set your energy up for the day and make you arrive at the office raring to go. Doing it after work will ground you again in your body after working with your mind all day, and relax you. But in these days of heightened awareness of health, there are many more alternatives generally available than in the past. You might, for example, prefer aikido (see p 100), or aerobics, both so popular now that you should have no difficulty in finding a class to join near the area in which you live.

Dancing is an excellent form of exercise, but only if you dance freely and expressively, rather than sticking to prescribed steps. You can do it whenever you want to at home – and to virtually any sort of music. Whatever music you choose to play, surrender to it and allow your body to move any way it wants to. Fast or funky rock (especially if played loudly) will get your energy moving very quickly. If noise is a problem where you live, use a Walkman. Allowing your body to flow to more 'floaty music' like New Age on the other hand will leave you more relaxed afterwards. Whichever music you dance to, it will leave you less jaded and more grounded.

How much exercise you take will depend on your age and physical condition. It is important (especially if you have not exercised for ages) not to overdo things. If in doubt you should have a check-up with your doctor before you embark on any exercise programme. And even if your physical condition is below par or you are convalescing you can still exercise your muscles by stretching exercises, for example by adopting yoga postures that we shall be describing shortly. The important thing is to give your muscles work to do if you want to prevent your energy from becoming stagnant. And, even if you feel tired, sleeping is not always the answer. Energy is not like money, once you spend it it's gone. The more energy we use, the more we get.

Ideally, one should try to get some sort of exercise every day. This is not as hard as it sounds. For example, walking is one of the best forms of exercise there is. If you can walk a mile every day this will help you keep your energy flowing. Remember though to walk briskly rather than to slouch along. And if you can't manage a mile every day, at least choose to walk rather than, say, to catch the bus, at least for part of the way. Quite apart from giving you exercise and filling your lungs, walking will help to counteract some of the unhealthy effects of spending too long sitting at your desk like impaired circulation that can produce haemorrhoids or swollen ankles (oedema). Cycling to work also will do the trick – if you can put up with the fumes of the traffic and the contempt with which most car drivers treat cyclists.

In the following pages we shall be describing how you can exercise whenever you need to without leaving the house. Remember the principles we have mentioned. They are:

- Oxygenating the body by deep breathing.
- Becoming aware of the body again.
- Giving muscles work to do.
- Slowing down thinking.

Here are some ways to do this, taken from yoga.

BREATHING EXERCISES

Bellows breath

Benefits: oxygenates all the cells of the body.
Stand up, clench your fists and start breathing rapidly through your
nose. Use your whole body and let your arms help you to pump air in
and out. Go on as long as you can and stop when you feel tired. Let
your body move with your breathing. About five minutes is usually
enough.

Stretching and breathing

Benefits: very centring.
Link your hands together, interlocking fingers. Now stretch your
arms out in front of you and up above your head, as high as you can
reach. As you do so, take a long, deep breath. Hold for a count of five,
then bring your linked hands down behind your neck, then up again
above your head again, and then back to the starting position with
your hands linked in front of you. Breathe out slowly as you come
down. Try to fill your lungs to their full capacity. Repeat the exercise
for as many times as feels good.

   A variation on this is to finish with your arms by your sides rather
than in front of you.

Alternate nostril breathing

Benefits: balances yin and yang energies.
Sit or kneel down. Close the right nostril with the right thumb and
breathe deeply in through the left nostril. Hold the breath for a count
of five. Then, with the right index finger, close the left nostril, let go of
the right nostril and breathe out through it. Still keeping the right
index finger closing the left nostril, breathe in through the right nostril. Now close the right nostril with the right thumb – and breathe
out through the left nostril.

Hara breathing

Benefits: centring, calming, invigorating.

In the east, the centre of our body and of our vital energies is considered to be the hara, the area below the navel and above the pubis. The 'man with hara' is considered to be not easily thrown off balance. He is energetic, with stamina, confident and 'gutsy'. How to centre in the hara is one of the basic things one learns in the martial arts. We can energise the hara in a number of ways. Breathing into it is one.

Sit with your hands on your hara. Start breathing in and out into the lower belly, giving particular emphasis to the incoming breath. Imagine there is a balloon in your lower belly which you alternately inflate and deflate. Continue for as long as feels comfortable.

These breathing exercises are extraordinarily powerful, don't overdo them. Don't force or strain, and stop when it feels right. If your fingers start to tingle this is a sign that you are hyperventilating. Stop *immediately*. It would not be advisable to do these deep-breathing exercises if you have a cold or suffer from heart, sinus or chest complaints.

YOGA POSTURES

After your breathing exercises, try a few postures from *hatha yoga*. Yoga is the art *par excellence* of accumulating energy. Unlike western forms of exercise aimed at developing muscles and stamina, hatha yoga uses postures which work on the endocrine and nervous systems. Stretching forms a big part of these postures. Yogis in India developed the system from observing animals, which is why some of them have the names they do, like the Lion Posture (there are still lions in Gujarat Province), the Cobra Posture and so on. Think of the way your cat stretches and arches its back after waking up from a nap and how it is very rarely off-balance, and you will get some idea of what yoga is about. Even after a very short session of assuming these postures you will feel more centred, energised and refreshed. Don't strain while you are doing them. *Relax* into them.

These yoga postures are good for all parts of the body. They tone the muscles, relax the nerves, maintain the joints, make the spine more supple, strengthen bones and inner organs, and release physical and psychic tension. Not only that, but regular practice of yoga will make you look, as well as feel, younger!

The Folded Leaf

Get down on to your knees and assume a foetal position, cupping your head in your hands on the floor in front of you. Your elbows should be on the floor. Stay in this posture for as long as you wish, for it is very soothing.

The Cobra

From the Folded Leaf, stretch your whole length out on the floor, resting the upper part of your body on your forearms, hands flat on the floor in front of you. Belly, thighs and knees remain in contact with the floor throughout this posture. Pressing on hands and forearms, raise your torso as high as is comfortable – and then a little more. While in this position, raise your chin and and protrude your tongue as far as it will go. This exercises the face muscles, something we rarely do. Hold the posture for as long as feels comfortable, then return to the prone position full-length on the floor again. Rest for a few moments, then repeat. Feel your spine arching. Repeat several times.

The Shoulderstand

Roll over on to your back, draw both knees up, and, using your arms to support your back, lever yourself up into an inverted position, supporting your weight on your shoulders. Your hands should now move up to the small of your back so that you can hold this position. Point your toes towards the ceiling. Stay like this in the inverted position for a few seconds only and relax into it. Then come down *slowly* and rest on your back in the Corpse Posture (see below).

Do not attempt the shoulderstand if you suffer from high blood pressure, and stop immediately if you experience dizziness or black spots before the eyes.

This posture is particularly good to do if you have varicose veins or if your legs ache because you have been on your feet all day. It also reverses the pull of gravity on the internal organs and refreshes the lungs, face and brain with increased blood circulation. It is claimed that, if you do it regularly, it will even make you look younger!

The Corpse Posture

This is a good one to try after the shoulderstand. It is very simple, and consists of lying on your back and relaxing, arms by your sides with palms up-turned and eyes closed (Fig 1). This posture is the basis for almost all relaxation techniques. We shall be describing some of these in the next chapter.

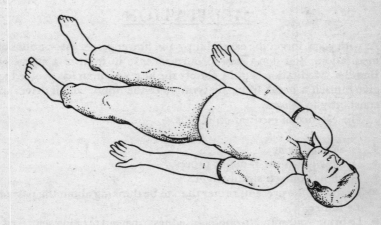

Fig 1   *Corpse Posture*

The Tree

This is a little harder to do than the other postures described above, but it is well worth doing if you can because it is so centring.

Stand with your feet shoulder-width apart. Bring up the right foot and lodge the heel in the left groin so that it stays there without slipping down. Keep the foot there, interlock the fingers of both hands and raise your arms high above your head, as high as you can go (as in the first breathing exercise described above). Fix your gaze on a point in front of you, just above eye-level. You will probably wobble at first, so to be on the safe side do this posture close to a wall or bookcase so that you can get some support if needed.

Hold the posture for as long as you can and feel your spine being stretched. Then come out of the posture *slowly*, using your hands to release your foot. Repeat the posture, this time with the left heel in the right groin.

If you decide you want to learn more postures, you could either sign up for a class or learn them from the many books on yoga.

Doing these postures will have calmed you down and centred your energy. This is a good time to meditate for a while.

MEDITATION

As with yoga, forget the exotic hippy and flower power associations of meditation. You don't *have* to burn incense in front of a statue of Buddha. Meditation is quite simply the best way man has evolved to give himself a break from the tyranny of the mind, which drives us constantly to *do more*.

The essence of meditation is thus:

- To stop all *doing*.
- To slow down the thought process.
- To allow yourself simply to *be*.
- To stay in the present, rather than to be thinking about the past or the future.
- To bring your mind to one-pointedness, instead of being scattered.

We are where our attention is. Most of the time many of us are not really *here* at all. Our bodies are always in the now but we are not. And the busier your day has been, the more your attention has been pulled out by one thing after another, the less likely you are to be here-now. We have been conditioned to have and to do. Meditation is about relaxing from all effort, and just allowing yourself to be for a change. Sitting quietly, doing nothing (which is how meditation is described in Zen) allows your energy to accumulate again, for you stop leaking it. It is a relief, and well worth devoting time to a regular session every day.

WHAT REGULAR MEDITATION
<u>CAN DO FOR YOU</u>

Physical benefits:
- Decreases tension.
- Clears up psychosomatic ailments caused by tension.
- Protects against stress diseases.
- Lowers blood pressure.
- Strengthens immune system.
- Slows down the ageing process.
- Recharges batteries.

Psychological benefits:
- Calms.
- Soothes.
- Energises.
- Distances from worries.
- Integrates.
- Brings clarity.
- Enhances sense of self.
- Promotes personal growth.

Benefits for work:
- More total concentration.
- Less capacity for being distracted.
- Improved memory.
- Quicker learning (eg languages).
- Staying centred when under pressure.
- Facilitates the flow of creative ideas.

Benefits for play:
- Heightened enjoyment through the senses.
- Present-centredness.
- Capacity for total involvement.
- Non-seriousness.

Benefits for relating:
- More self-confidence.
- More tolerance.
- More sensitivity.
- More authenticity.

A few tips before you start:

Timing

Try to keep to the same time each day. Don't try to meditate after a meal (especially a heavy one), or after drinking coffee or alcohol. Either you will fall asleep or the caffeine will make you feel restless. The point of meditating is to remain relaxed *and* alert. I have found that my best times for meditation are either before lunch or before the evening meal. To begin with, 20 minutes is about right.

Place

Anywhere that is quiet and where you will not be disturbed for the length of the session will do. Try to keep to the same place each time. Meditating regularly in the same room builds up peaceful vibrations there which will make it easier for you to slip into a meditative space.

Posture

You have a choice. Whichever one you choose, make sure you are comfortable. Meditation is meant to be enjoyed, not endured.

If you are supple enough, sit cross-legged on a firm cushion. Try to keep your knees on the floor. You will probably need two cushions to raise your buttocks high enough to make this possible. If you can, place the left foot on the right thigh and the right foot on the left thigh. This is called the 'Full Lotus Posture' and is illustrated in Fig 2. Don't worry if this is quite beyond you – the Half Lotus is just as good, with only one foot on the other thigh (Fig 3) or resting in the hollow between the thigh and the calf (Fig 4). If it is excruciating for you to get one foot on the thigh you can just sit cross-legged, tailor-fashion, but this position is not quite so grounding as the others.

Another good posture (and one that you can switch into if your legs begin to ache halfway through the session) is kneeling. Rest your buttocks on your heels, and if you wish, have a small cushion under you. Alternatively, you could meditate sitting on a chair or a meditation stool. The back should be kept straight (without straining), and this applies to all the meditation postures. If using a chair, sit on the edge of it, don't lean against the back of the chair. And keep your feet flat on the floor – don't cross them.

In each of these postures your hands can be either on the thighs

Fig 2 *Full Lotus Posture*

Fig 3 *Half Lotus Posture*

Fig 4 *Half Lotus Posture*

(palms either up or down), or joined lightly together in front of you on the pubis, left hand in right and with the tips of the thumbs touching.

The eyes are usually kept closed during meditation, except in gazing (tratak), sitting (zazen) or *raja yoga* meditations.

MEDITATION TECHNIQUES

Really, all you are doing, whichever technique you adopt, is slowing down your thought process by giving your mind something to occupy it, usually by focussing relaxed attention on one thing.

Listening

Just that. What sounds are you aware of right now? Can you hear the hum of traffic? A radio playing somewhere else in the house? The ticking of the clock on the mantelpiece? Whichever sounds come into your awareness, listen to them without identifying them, just as if they were different instruments in an orchestra. Don't allow yourself to be disturbed by any of them, to wish they were not there. Make them a part of your meditation, for they are part of what is happening here – now – which is where you want to be. Be like your ears, totally passive, and let all the sounds in, impartially.

Gazing (tratak)

Once again, it does not matter what the object of your gazing is, provided it does not have disturbing associations for you. It could be a bowl of flowers set on the floor in front of you, a lighted candle, or a picture, devotional or otherwise.

Do not strain your eyes trying to see anything new or special about the object. Just look, keeping your eyes very soft, very relaxed. Remember that the object of your meditation is not to see anything special, but simply to slow down your mind.

A variation of this technique is to simply let your gaze wander round the room, taking in different things in turn. This is very grounding and brings you back into the present, especially if your mind is extremely active and driving you crazy.

Watching your thoughts (vipassana)

This is the purest form of meditation – to be aware of what you are thinking without valuing any thought above another, and not being 'hooked' by any of them into feeling you have to do anything about them. This just 'letting them be' demands the same type of passive awareness that is needed for Listening meditation – except that you are listening to the chatter inside your head instead of external sounds. Just witnessing in this way is the most passive activity a human being can engage in. In fact, it is not an activity, a 'doing', at all, but a 'non-doing', which is why I call it the purest form of meditation, for non-doing is ultimately what meditation is about.

When we witness in this way we become aware of just how much we talk to ourselves inside our heads. This inner chatter is endless – and never gets anywhere. It is a jumble of memories of the past and fantasies about the future, disjointed and haphazard. These thought bubbles tempt us like the Sirens to follow them – but they never lead anywhere, except into more thinking. In the East they think of the mind as a monkey, endlessly chattering and leaping about, never still. One of the biggest boons afforded by regular meditation is the realisation that we are not our minds and do not have to be controlled and manipulated by them. We can *choose* which thoughts are worth giving attention to – and let the rest fade away, which is what they will do if we do not feed them with attention. Meditation is the only way to break our identification with our minds, and this freedom brings less worry and more serenity into our daily lives.

Mantra meditation

This is probably the most popular form of meditation as it is the basis of TM (Transcendental Meditation). Focussing attention on a word or phrase and repeating it to oneself silently over and over again is an effective way of stilling the mind. It does not really matter what the word or words are, providing once again that they do not have disturbing associations for you. Think of them as a toy that one gives the mind to play with, in the same way that one does to pacify a fractious child. While it is thus occupied it is unable to drive us to distraction.

So choose your own mantra, preferably a short word or phrase that suggests relaxation to you. Some examples would be:

- peace
- love
- relax
- still.

If you are a Christian you could use the mantra 'Jesus' which is used in the Russian Orthodox Church, where it is known as the 'prayer of the Heart' or 'Jesus Prayer'.

Feel the mantra resonate in your body as you repeat it, either in your heart or in your hara – and feel yourself getting calmer by the minute.

Chanting

Chanting is similar to mantra meditation, except that one chants aloud rather than silently, and that usually more words are used. These are usually of a devotional nature, and it is claimed for them that they have a power in themselves to purify our energy, quite apart from the hypnotic effect of simple repetition.

The most well-known chant is AUM, supposed to be the basic 'sound of the Universe'. It should be chanted in two syllables, like

AH-OOM, and prolonging the final M in a humming sound. Another you might like to try is NAM YO HO RENGE KO (which defies translation). Whichever one you choose, feel the sound resonating throughout your body.

'Just sitting' (zazen)

There is a *haiku* (a 17-syllable poem much quoted in Zen) that runs:

> Sitting quietly
> Doing nothing,
> Spring comes and the grass grows
> By itself.

The last part could easily also have read 'And energy accumulates', for nothing allows our energy to build up more than the complete cessation of 'doing'.

So just sit, eyes half-open and gaze resting on a point on the floor in front of you, and feel this happening. If your mind tries to stop you relaxing into just being, try counting each outgoing breath up to ten, and then start again. When your mind starts to slow down, focus your attention on the hara, and keep coming back to it whenever distractions occur.

'Third eye' meditation

This is one of the easiest forms of meditation, used in raja yoga. It consists simply of centring your awareness in the space between the eyebrows (the so-called 'third eye'), and withdrawing energy from 'body consciousness' into 'soul consciousness'. It is in fact to remember that we are all souls inhabiting (some would say 'imprisoned' in) a body. Raja yogis believe that all our unhappiness and tension is the result of forgetting who we really are and getting too caught up in worldly matters.

It is important to meditate regularly rather than spasmodically, or just when we feel like it. Disciplining yourself to do this is well worth it – and the more you meditate, the easier it gets.

MEDITATION IN ACTION

Try to keep the 'meditative space' even when you are not actually sitting in meditation. The energy you have built up, the serenity, the centredness, can easily be squandered or scattered again by worrying or rushing in the course of the day. 'Staying meditative' means:

- Doing one thing at a time – totally.
- Staying aware of what you are doing (instead of thinking about other things while you are doing it).
- Staying centred in the midst of your work.
- Being aware of WHO is working (ie YOU).
- Not rushing, giving yourself time.
- Giving yourself time to respond rather than reacting blindly and automatically.
- Staying in touch with your body sensations.

Of course this is a counsel of perfection. Apart from enlightened beings, few of us can remain so aware all the time. But the alternative is to constantly be leaking energy so that by the end of the working day you feel drained. It is not much benefit to you to build up your energy if you are going to throw it away again.

4

RECHARGING BATTERIES

Learn to recognise the signs your system may be giving you that you are overdoing things and that your energy needs replenishing for example, are you:

- Getting enough sleep?
- Suffering from insomnia?
- Feeling drained a lot of the time?
- Finding it hard to unwind after work?
- Easily irritated, without knowing why?
- A workaholic?

Sleep is 'the great restorer' of energy, and we should make sure we get enough of it. It is a very personal thing and some of us need more than others. But it may in fact be less than you think. Research has shown that the average person needs six hours. But some people manage very well on less. While she was Prime Minister Mrs Thatcher, for example, apparently found four hours quite enough. She retired with her boxes at 2 am and got up for work at 6 am. Winston Churchill got by on three or four hours a night. It must be added, however, that he had the gift of being able to doze off at the drop of a hat – usually during the more dreary Cabinet meetings. Napoleon, too, was a catnapper, which enabled him to rise in the early hours of the morning. There is a painting of him in his study with the candle low and the clock behind him registering 4 am. Voltaire managed on three hours a night, so did Harry Truman. Anita Roddick, the founder of the Body Shop, claims she needs only four or five hours' sleep a night – and can manage on less. Her success and the fact that recently she was voted 'Businesswoman of the Year' suggest that having so little sleep is certainly not interfering with her efficiency.

There is an old adage that 'the hours of sleep before midnight are the best'. It is certainly true that the quality of our sleep changes during the night. During the first two-thirds of, say, eight hours' sleep we go in and out of deep and light sleep, whereas in the final third deep sleep is not usually present. Rapid eye movements (REM) recur about every 90 minutes or so, and it is during these periods that we dream.

INSOMNIA

If you suffer from insomnia it may be some consolation to know that you are in distinguished company. Famous insomniacs include Kafka, Kipling, Lord Rosebery, Pushkin and Proust. Also, research shows that there is no lasting physical damage from lack of sleep, though subjects forced to go without sleep for more than two nights in a row suffered lapses of concentration and became unable to perform mental tasks efficiently. It seems that it is the brain rather than the body that suffers. The body appears to be restored by simple rest, as opposed to sleep.

Alas, no fool-proof cure has been found for insomnia. Here, however, are a few tips that seem to work for some people.

1 Establish a natural sleep rhythm. Go to bed at the same time each night.

2 Don't eat heavy meals shortly before retiring, or drink stimulating beverages like tea or coffee late in the day. Instead, drink herb teas. Camomile is particularly soothing.

3 Practise deep relaxation just before going to bed, and, if you can, during the day also (see below for deep relaxation techniques).

4 Make sure you are getting enough exercise. Your body may just not be tired enough to sleep.

5 Avoid intellectual stimulation in the evenings. What is needed is right-side brain activity, not left-side (see page 59).

6 Make sure the bedroom is neither too cold nor over-heated, and is sufficiently well-ventilated.

7 Make sure you are totally comfortable in bed. Check out whether your mattress is either too hard, lumpy, or too soft – and get a new one. Sleep with your head pointing north as this is supposed to align you with the earth's magnetic meridians.

8 When in bed, breathe more slowly, and count the outgoing breaths. Practise progressive body relaxation (see page 54).

9 Have a tape recorder by your bed and play softly a 'relaxation tape'. We shall be discussing these later: the tape can be either of the 'talk you down' variety or of New Age music or environmental sounds (eg the ocean, or running water). If your bedmate objects, use a Walkman.

10 For some reason, I have found (on the rare occasions I have difficulty in sleeping) that keeping one foot or leg outside the duvet helps.

If you are really desperate (because, for example, it is important that you be on top form next day) resist the temptation to take barbiturates. Rather, take herbal sleeping pills. Baldrian, which contains valerian, a plant known for centuries for its ability to induce sleep, is particularly good, and won't leave you 'hung-over' next morning. As it is not a chemical, it is totally non-addictive. You might also try a homeopathic remedy, such as aconitum, arnica or camomile. Also, programme yourself for a good night's sleep. One of the things that happens with insomnia is that we get anxious about it, and the more anxious, the more tense we become. It becomes a vicious circle. Tell yourself that tonight you will sleep like a baby. This is an example of affirmations that we shall be discussing later on.

Do not take naps during the day. No deep sleep is taken during a typical nap. Dr Jim Horne of Loughborough University, a psychologist who has done much research into sleeping patterns, warns us particularly to beware of napping so long during the day that we begin to experience deep sleep. Your body will switch off and on being awakened you will find yourself feeling awful. This is because your body assumes that after half-an-hour there's a full eight hours' sleep coming along. This has the same effect as when you go to sleep at night and are awakened after a few hours.

If, then, we are not to take naps during the day when we feel fatigued or drained, how are we to recharge our batteries? The answer is, instead of sleeping, to practise deep relaxation. By 'deep' we mean total, psychophysical relaxation (ie of mind and emotions as well as of the body) not just 'putting your feet up'. Before we describe how to do this let us first look at what happens when we relax deeply.

WHAT HAPPENS WHEN WE
PRACTISE DEEP RELAXATION?

When we relax, really relax, we let go of what neurologist W.B. Cannon called the 'fight or flight' response (associated with anger or anxiety) and sink into what Dr Herbert Benson, an American professor who researched the mechanics of tension and relaxation, called the 'relaxation response'. The parasympathetic (involuntary) branch of the autonomic nervous system takes over from the sympathetic (voluntary) branch. Breathing slows down, heart rate and blood pressure lower, muscles relax . . . There is also a decrease in blood lactate and an increase of the skin's resistance to a mild electric current. These are significant because high-blood lactate and low-skin resistance are associated with anxiety states. In short, our tension evaporates as we 'switch off', slow down, unwind during our deep relaxation session.

Changes also happen in brainwave activity that are quite different from 'just resting' or sleep patterns. They have been measured using an electroencephalograph (usually abbreviated to EEG). We spend most of our working day (and perhaps most of our waking state) functioning on the beta wavelength. This means that the electrical activity in our brains is varying within the range of 14 to 26 times per second (usually measured as cycles per second, indicated by the symbol Hz). If we are having a hard day at the office we will be high on the beta scale rather than low, for the greater the effort or stress, the higher and faster the frequency.

Beta is our 'everyday mind', associated with thinking, planning, doing, concentrating, problem-solving and generally focussing upon the outside world and meeting its demands upon us. The beta state is not a particularly unpleasant or uncomfortable state to be in (except perhaps on a rainy Monday morning queueing to get the bus – and especially if you are late for work). If, however, you go too high in beta, or stay too long in it, you will be 'speedy', uptight, and find it hard to unwind and relax when you do take a break.

When we relax our brainwaves start to slow down to the lower frequency of 8 to 13Hz that we call alpha. Just as beta is associated with being 'on the go', so the alpha state is experienced as one of wellbeing, of having space and not being under pressure. It will be familiar to all of us as 'that holiday feeling' or when we are having a good time. The more we relax, the deeper we go into the alpha state. If we feel so euphoric that we start to doze off we have entered the theta wavelength (below 7Hz), the half-asleep or dreaming state. When we are in deep, dreamless sleep our brainwaves have slowed down to between 0.5 and 4Hz, which is the delta range.

'But what', you may be asking yourself, 'is the difference between that and what happens when I just put my feet up, or take a nap?' The answer is that the decrease in your metabolic rate happens much faster when you are in alpha than when you are sleeping. In alpha the rate of decrease of oxygen consumption averages between 10% and 20% and occurs within a few minutes of starting to relax. When we sleep, on the other hand, our consumption of oxygen decreases only slowly. After four or five hours it is still only about 8% lower than when we were awake. Also lactate concentration in the blood decreases almost four times as quickly as it does if you are just 'putting your feet up', while skin resistance has been found in some cases to increase as much as 400%.

So make a habit of treating yourself to a session of deep relaxation at least once a day. There is nothing like it for recharging your batteries. Here's how to do it:

- Slow down your breathing.
- Focus on positive, reassuring images in your mind.
- Become more aware of your body.
- Allow your brain activity to slow down.

If this seems similar in some ways to meditation, it is. What they have in common is that they both get you into the alpha state. But, unless you are an experienced meditator, deep relaxation gets you there faster. With practice you can train yourself to sink down into alpha within a few minutes or so.

ALPHA RELAXATION TECHNIQUE

Prepare for your relaxation session by withdrawing to a quiet room. Tell your family or whoever you live with that you do not want to be disturbed for at least half-an-hour, that you will not be answering the telephone and the caller should ring back later.

Make yourself really comfortable. Have the intention to shelve your problems for these few moments and tell yourself that you will be better able to deal with them after refreshing your brain and when you have more energy.

I prefer to lie on my back during a relaxation session, but you may prefer to lie on your side instead. Become aware of your breathing: make it deeper and slower. Start to count the *outgoing* breath up to 'ten' – then start again at 'one'. Imagine that you are in natural surroundings where you feel happy and safe. You could picture, for example, a secluded beach, or a beautiful garden. Any scene that is restful and makes you feel good will do.

Enjoy this fantasy for a few minutes. As thinking slows down and energy begins to seep down from your head into your body you will start to become aware of body sensations. Now is the time to start relaxing your body, each part in turn.

Progressive body relaxation

Body awareness is crucial for relaxation. The more in your head you are, the less relaxed you will be.

Start with the left foot. Without moving it, let your attention go to the toes of one foot, one after another. Feel their shape and size (you don't need to wiggle them – feel them from the *inside*). Now feel the rest of the foot: heel, sole, ankle . . . Take your time, for the whole point of relaxing is to free yourself from the pressure of time for a while.

Now feel the weight of the whole foot resting on the mattress. Let your attention move up to the lower leg. Feel your calf muscle. Is it tense or relaxed? If the former, let yourself experience the tension before letting the muscle get heavy, expanding, softer . . . Move up the leg to the thigh. Once again, feel any tension there – and let go of it. Feel the difference now between the relaxed leg and the unrelaxed one.

Repeat the whole sequence with the other leg, starting again with the foot and the toes. Feel the tension in each part – and let go of it.

When you have relaxed both legs, give attention in the same way to the other parts of your body. The following would be a logical sequence to follow:

- buttocks
- anus and genitals
- lower back
- spine
- shoulders.

Let those big back muscles get heavy and sink into the mattress. Continue with:

- left upper arm
- left lower arm
- left hand and fingers
- right upper arm
- right lower arm
- right hand and fingers.

Get the feeling of letting go of your arms, as if they did not belong to you. Then do:

- chest (give a big sigh or two)
- abdomen (this will often be the most tense part of your body, so allow plenty of time to relax it. Feel it expanding, melting, opening . . .).

Finally, feel the tension that is almost certainly likely to be there in your face, the result of the masks we all have to put on in order to 'face the world' – to do our jobs and hide our vulnerability. Relax your scalp, and the muscles around the eyes. Let these sink deep into your head . . . Relax your jaw and your tongue. Let your mouth sag open. Nobody is watching.

By now you will be feeling calm, relaxed and in touch with your body. Stay like this for as long as you can, for resting in alpha is doing a whole lot of good for you in counteracting the effects of stress and building up your energy again. An 'alpha a day' does indeed keep the doctor away. Here are some other ways to achieve alpha – though it is not so much an achievement as a 'letting go'.

BATHING

Bathing is a time-honoured way of unwinding. The ancient Greeks did it, the Romans institutionalised it, the Moors and the Turks still do. Sometimes it is the only way of getting precious space to ourselves for a while. The privacy of the bathroom is universally respected. People accept that if we are having a bath they cannot expect us to answer the door or the phone. The relaxing effect of bathing is not only that warm water expands us, or that a cold shower invigorates us, but also that immersing ourselves in water purifies our energy field as well.

It was Fritz Perls, the founder of Gestalt therapy, who said that we have to 'lose our minds and come to our senses'. One of the ways we can be good to ourselves is to turn bathtime into a deliciously sensual experience rather than just a cleaning ritual. Put a tape of your favourite music on a tape recorder, switch off the overhead light and set a lighted candle or nightlight on the edge of the bath. Perfume the water with a fragrant oil. Aromatherapists tell us that certain oils have especially relaxing properties, for example, sandalwood, lavender, rose and cedarwood. If you don't have any of these, try massaging olive oil into your skin before you step into the bath. It will leave your skin soft and smooth when you get out again. Don't have the water too hot or this could be enervating. Soak and enjoy. Afterwards, if you wish, you can take a cold shower – a specially good thing to do if you have an engagement to go to as it will wake you up again.

MASSAGE

Massage is good for you. It promotes vitality and relaxation by toning the muscles, removing toxins and stimulating the circulation. Above all, it feels good. There is no substitute for being massaged by a professional masseur for getting us into awareness of our bodies. If you can afford it, find a good one (usually by recommendation) and get him or her to visit. Otherwise you could ask a friend to give you a back, foot or face massage, or, if your intimacy is such, a full body massage. Some friends of mine do this on a reciprocal basis and take it in turns to exchange massage once a week. To end up with a nice dinner and a bottle of wine makes for a very civilised and satisfying evening.

It is easy to learn the basic strokes, and you can help each other by saying which parts of your body are tense and need particular attention. It is more convenient and less back-breaking to do massage on a *firm* mattress on the floor than on a bed, assuming neither of you has a massage table. Make sure you are warm enough. Have a blanket handy to cover up the parts of the body that are not being massaged at any moment to avoid getting chilled.

Provided that you are sensitive to the person you are massaging, have warmed your hands – and cut your nails – before venturing to lay a finger on him or her, you won't go far wrong. Try to get in tune with each other before you start. One way of doing this is to synchronise your breathing rhythms. Stay in physical contact throughout the massage. For example, if you need more oil, keep one hand in contact with the other person while you reach for the bottle. It can be a little disturbing to be suddenly jabbed from out of nowhere. Soft music, preferably instrumental or New Age (see page 59) also helps to create the right mood.

A good sequence to follow would be:

- neck
- back
- arms
- legs
- feet
- face and scalp.

Be especially gentle and sensitive when you massage the face, for this is one of the most vulnerable parts of the body and an 'attacking' approach can feel quite threatening. On the other hand, when you do the back you can be as firm as you like. The best book on massage technique I know is *The Book of Massage* (see Bibliography).

Don't massage or be massaged on a full stomach, and don't disperse the good energy you have accumulated by bathing or showering afterwards – better to bathe before. Keep talking down to a minimum to keep the energy 'in' and to facilitate the descent to alpha. Having to respond to questions will keep you both in left-side brain, so don't gossip! After being massaged, lie quietly for as long as you want and allow yourself to enjoy how your body now feels.

SELF MASSAGE

If there is no-one around to give you a massage try doing it yourself. Here's how.

Face and scalp massage

Rub your hands together to get energy into them and to warm them up.

Place them over your face. Rub the hands together again, and repeat. The soothing effect can also be gained by applying hot towels or flannels to your face. Make sure they are not too hot.

Start to massage your scalp. Rather than rubbing, use the finger-tips to move the skin of the scalp.

Smooth the forehead, from the frown lines outwards to the hairline. Press firmly with the middle fingers of both hands.

Massage your temples with third and fourth fingers, using small circular movements.

If your jaw feels tight, make fists and press the knuckles into the hollows below the cheekbones, using a circular motion.

Meridian massage

Meridians, you will remember, are the pathways along which energy flows through the body (see the illustrations on pages 93–95). We can stimulate the flow of energy along them by massaging in the direction that the energy flows, as follows.

Using firm pressure, run both hands simultaneously down the outside of both thighs and legs and, in one flowing movement, up the inside of the legs and thighs. Repeat several times.

Starting from the back of the left hand and fingers, run the right palm up the *back* of the left arm and down the *inside* of the left arm. Finish the stroke with a flick of the right hand off the fingers of the left. Repeat several times, then work with the left hand on the right arm.

Following the energy flow in this way stimulates your energy. If on the other hand you have more energy than you can handle, are rest-less and off centre, reversing the direction of your massaging will calm you down.

Foot massage

A great one to do if your feet ache after being on them for too long – and very soothing generally.

Grasp one foot with both hands, palms and thumbs on top of the instep. Squeeze the sole all over as firmly as you can with your fingers.

Make a fist and screw it hard into the ball of the foot and under the instep.

Pinch the skin between each toe in turn.

Pull each toe in turn, squeezing it as you pull and finishing with a 'snap'.

MUSIC

Listening to (or playing) music is one of the easiest ways for many people of getting into the alpha state. It stimulates feeling and thus moves us out of left-hemisphere brain functioning into right, out of our minds and into our senses. As well as being a great mood-changer, music produces physiological changes: lower blood pressure, slower pulse rate, increased flow of gastric juices.

Experiments have shown that, for the purposes of relaxation, instrumental is better than vocal music, probably because there are no words that we have to think about. Baroque music is apparently the rest, and Mozart the best of all for helping us unwind.

There are tapes on the market expressly designed to aid relaxation and it would be a good idea to investigate them to see which ones appeal to you. This type of music is called 'New Age', and instruments used usually include synthesisers, flutes, harps, chimes . . . Sometimes composers add a background of soothing environmental sounds (eg runninng water, birdsong) or you can buy tapes with just these on. My personal favourite is 'Slow Ocean', that consists simply of the ebb and flow of waves on a beach. It is deeply relaxing and very much an alpha producer. You can usually try out the tapes in the shop before you choose them.

DANCING

One of the quickest ways to change your mood if you are feeling down and depressed is to dance. Dancing gets you into your body as nothing else can, and is in fact one of the best meditations there is, to lose yourself in the dancing. From African tribesmen and Sufi dervishes to the modern discotheque, people have always got high on it.

Put on music you like, preferably with a strong rhythmic beat (though really one can dance to virtually anything). Let your body move any way it wants to. Surrender to it, and to the music. On a good day you will get to feeling more and more blissful as you dance and let go of your tensions and worries. Be like Zorba the Greek!

If noise is a problem for the people you live with, use a walkman. Dance barefoot, with as few clothes on as possible, and ecstatically. Really use your body – dance totally. Afterwards lie down, close your eyes and feel how much more alive you are, and the energy coursing throughout your body.

NATURE

One of the things that makes us feel jaded is to be too much in the city, with its noise, crowds and perpetual rush. So get out to the country as often as you can. Go for long walks. Enjoy the freshness of the air, the trees, the flowers, the birds singing their hearts out. Relax on your back and watch the clouds moving majestically across the sky . . .

If you can't leave town right now, at least use the parks. And if you are confined to your home for some reason, you can still have lots of indoor plants . . . Talk to them, be with them, enjoy them. Also, your pets. Dr Aaron Katche of Pennsylvania University has found that petting an animal to which one is bonded leads to lower blood pressure.

Enjoyment is in fact the key to alpha, quite apart from being very good for your immune system. Enjoy as much as you can. As far as possible only do things you enjoy doing – and try to enjoy the things that you just *have* to do. Resistance saps energy.

5

HANDLING NEGATIVE ENERGY

Anger is one of the hardest feelings for most people to handle. Very few of us feel comfortable with it. We fear that it might swamp us, that if we confront the object of our anger they will never speak to us again, and so forth. And, of course, if we are angry with the boss and tell him or her what we really think of them, we may well be out of a job.

What do you do with your anger? Do you:

- Swallow it?
- Dump it on subordinates?
- Complain and blame?
- Nag?
- Throw a tantrum?
- Sulk?
- Kick the cat?

How do you react if somebody is angry with *you*?

- Get angry as well?
- Try to appease them?
- Run away?
- Feel that you are a Bad Person?
- Get depressed?

And yet anger is just a form of energy, and all our energies are there for some purpose. We may be totally justified in feeling angry. Somebody may have treated us or people we love shabbily, invalidated or misjudged us, or invaded our space. We usually feel angry when we feel threatened in some way. The purpose of anger is to protect us – and it could well save our lives one day. Without the capacity to be angry we are pushovers – and will not be respected for it, or respect ourselves. Its basis is the rush of adrenalin, designed to gear us for fight or flight.

REPRESSION

The problem is not anger, but what to do with it. It should never be repressed. The adrenalin will simply poison our bodies and depress our immune system. Dr Carl Simonton, an American cancer specialist and author of *Getting Well Again*, discovered that the typical cancer patient evinces a strong tendency to harbour resentment, a reluctance to forgive, and a habit of self-pity. In a similar survey a New York psychologist, Lawrence LeShan, found in a survey of 250 cancer patients that all suffered from feelings of self-hatred (ie anger turned inwards, against themselves) and inability to come to their own defence if attacked (ie not being able to put out their anger).

Suppressed anger solidifies into resentment and victim consciousness. The suppressed anger energy remains trapped in our muscles, making us tense. Dr Wouter Osterhuis of the University of Amsterdam investigated patients complaining of pain for which there was no obvious physical cause. Of 331 with suppressed feelings of aggression, 329 suffered from pains in the neck, nine out of ten who experienced fear had abdominal pains and six out of ten with lower back pains were experiencing despair. In case you find this alarming or depressing, take heart from Dr Ellerbroek (cited in Bernie Siegels' *Love, Medicine and Miracles*, see Bibliography). Ellerbroek described 57 well-documented cancer 'miracles' in which the cure followed the patients' conscious decision to give up their anger and depression. From that point their tumours started to shrink. In other words the harmful effects of long-standing negativity can be reversed – but only if we choose to let go of it.

CATHARSIS

What, then, to do when you are feeling really angry? Ideally one should confront the object of one's wrath and share with them how you are feeling and why. But of course this may not be possible or advisable. The first thing to do, however, is to acknowledge to yourself that you are angry, and then to find some way of discharging the energy without adding to your problems (which might well include feeling guilty if you 'dump', ie pick on someone who does not deserve it). The most important thing is to discharge the adrenalin from your body. You might try one or other of the following cathartic techniques developed in therapy groups when you are alone.

- Kneel on the floor with a large cushion in front of you and proceed to beat the hell out of it, either with your fists or with a tennis racquet. Put your whole body energy into the beating, raising your arms high each time. Let sounds come, the more savage the better. Go beyond the point where you feel like stopping until you feel purged of your anger.

- Strangle a small cushion.

- Wring the neck of a towel. Be as vicious as you know how. Let your body and facial expression express exactly how you feel.

- Throw a tantrum. Lie on your back on a mattress and beat it. Make fists and bring them down hard on to the mattress, not together, but alternately, left fist, right fist and so on. At the same time start kicking with your heels, once again alternately. Use your total energy, and let sounds come.

Note: Negative energy sticks around, so it is better not to throw your tantrum on the bed you will be sleeping in. Also, take a shower afterwards to wash off the negative energy.

If these aggressive outlets are not to your taste you could try:

- Going for a run.
- Going for a swim.
- Dancing energetically, preferably to loud and fast rock.

The important thing is to expel the anger energy in some way, without doing harm to others or to yourself. You don't even have to wait until you get home. Try screaming, shouting or swearing as you drive home from work. (Make sure however that the car windows are closed!)

These cathartic techniques I call the 'first aid' for anger, and they will certainly make you feel better. And purging the energy will make it easier for you to share later with the person who has offended you without blaming, complaining or dumping.

TIME AND SPACE MANAGEMENT

Much of our anger comes from frustration and being too much under pressure and one way of having more energy available is to stop leaking it because you are not sufficiently well organised. If you can't afford a good secretary, at least have a good filing system. Make sure you insert documents in the appropriate file (clearly labelled) *immediately* either on receipt or when you have finished with them. Always keep your telephone and address books in the same place so that you know where they are.

Here are a few tips to cut out unnecessary stress at work.

- Don't try to do too many things at the same time. Decide on your priorities – and stick to them.

- As far as possible, don't commit yourself to time limits for finishing a project – or accept other people's time limits. Working against time is one of the biggest drains on energy there is.

- On your way to work run over in your mind what you have to do today – and tell yourself that all is going to run smoothly. This is an example of affirmations (which we shall be discussing later) in which we programme ourselves to *expect* success in our projects.

- Have a system of trays containing the relevant documents needing your attention and arrange them in order of urgency. Include a tray for work completed, needing posting, or for handing on to somebody else.

- Arrange if you can to do the work demanding the most intensive concentration or creativity during the time of the day when you are at your sharpest, and do the routine stuff when your energy is flagging. Some people are semi-conscious in the mornings and improve as the day goes on. For me it is the reverse, so I write in the mornings and do routine editing and printing later in the day.

- Pace yourself. Do not concentrate for more than an hour and a half at a stretch. It has been found by psychologists that this is usually the maximum we can stand. Going on after that without a break produces errors. And research has shown that working harder, making more effort, does not make for more efficiency but simply more fatigue and stress. One study showed, for example, that lengthening your working day from eight to 12 hours can increase error rates by as much as 80%.

- Take short breaks every so often. Go to the washroom perhaps, move, stretch, breathe deeply, try some of the self-massage techniques described earlier . . .

- There are few things more infuriating than having to hold on while telephoning (especially long-distance), or waiting for somebody to ring back who doesn't. Never hold on if you make a call and the person you want is engaged. With important calls never agree to be called back. Instead, fix a time when you can call again.

- Bring some awareness to *how* you work, so that you don't leak energy by straining your eyes for example. If necessary, rearrange lighting and seating so that you feel more relaxed and comfortable.

- Be aware of your body posture from time to time. What goes on in the mind is always reflected in the body, and the effort of concentration makes us tighten up our muscles. Check, for example, whether your shoulders are hunched, and whether your back muscles are tight.

- Make sure you are getting enough oxygen and that the room in which you are working is well-ventilated.

WORRYING

Are you a compulsive worrier (ie do you always have *something* to worry about)?

- What are your catastrophic expectations?
- What sort of things do you tell yourself?
- What is the very worst that could happen?

Worrying is stressful and draining. It takes all the joy out of life and exhausts us physically and emotionally. It makes us look haggard and drawn, especially if we are losing appetite or sleep. It can also make us ill. Here are some ways of making it less lethal.

- The first thing to do with worry (and fear, which is really the basis of it), is to confront it head on. Bring your particular worry out into the open and have a good look at it. Articulate it, put it into words so that you know exactly what you are dealing with. Is it your health you are worried about, or that of somebody close to you? Is it money? Your job? What *exactly* are you afraid might happen? And if it does, so what?

    This 'so what?' is a powerful antidote to worry, for one gets to realise that one's catastrophic expectations are mostly quite unrealistic. You are not going to be put in jail just because you can't pay your bills right now. In this age of inflation and unemployment there are many, many people in the same position as you. Your creditors will just have to wait.

- Get support, either by sharing your worries with an understanding friend or seeking professional advice, whether medical, legal or financial. You are not alone in this world, though in your darkest moments it may feel that way.

- Ask yourself: 'What can I do about this situation?' Sit down with pen and paper and write down all the possibilities. Don't stop when you think you have exhausted all of these. Allow others to emerge from your subconscious, and practise a bit of lateral thinking, ie get out of the rut of thinking of your problem in only one way. At some level we always know what we have to do. Trust your intuition – and your dreams, which will often suggest new possibilities. Jung said that problems were never solved at the level they were formulated. We have to stop being locked in the polarities of seeing the possible solution as either 'this' or 'that', which he called 'thesis' and 'antithesis', and allow a 'synthesis' or 'higher third' to emerge from our Unconscious. When this happens – and the Unconscious cannot tolerate unfinished situations for long – problems are *dissolved* rather than solved, as new possibilities we had not thought of occur to us.

- Remind yourself that you have found yourself in desperate

situations before – and are still here to tell the tale. To counteract depression tell yourself 'This too shall pass' and that 'It always works out, so it must be working out *now*'.

- The most important thing (and one that will certainly make you feel better about your situation) is to get out of the victim space any way you can. Characteristic of victim consciousness is a feeling of hopelessness and helplessness, and of the world as somehow out to get you. Instead of wallowing in depression and playing 'Ain't it Awful', try to become aware of just how things were allowed to become so desperate in the first place. What was your own contribution to creating the energy that has constellated in this unpleasant fashion? What did you do, or what didn't you do that needed to be done? If you know where the real problem lies, you have that much better chance of solving it. If all you do is complain and blame, you have none. Take back your power. What you created you can uncreate. Sometimes, of course, we are hit by disasters that appear to be just accidents, and for which there is no way we can possibly have contributed to them. When your life is turning into a nightmare all that you can really constructively do is to treat it as a learning experience and trust that there is some higher reason for you being 'put through it'. Perhaps the 'point' of it is to strengthen you, or to raise your level of consciousness in some way. Certainly you will be a different person when you come out at the other end. As someone once said, 'What doesn't kill you, makes you stronger'.

- Trust that the Universe always gives us what we need – but only when we really need it. It is as if Life rushes to fill a perceived lack, and perhaps what you really lack is not what you think. I never think that the Universe understands *money*, for example, which after all is really only figures on a bank statement. But it does understand *feelings*, love and trust, for example, and it could be that you are being put through this experience to learn these. We are here to grow in consciousness, not to be without problems. Raise your sights a little. Praying for guidance always helps.

SELF-ESTEEM

Of all forms of negativity, that which we turn against ourselves is the most damaging. At least if someone else attacks us we can (hopefully) defend ourselves. When, however, the enemy is within, we are defenceless. Unless we love and validate ourselves nothing will ever go right for us, our health, our relationships, our career. We will wear ourselves out searching for the love, respect and appreciation from outside. But unless we first give these to ourselves we will never experience them. We won't trust them, probably won't even notice them.

Continuously harbouring negative thoughts about ourselves castrates our energy, confidence and optimism. It predisposes us to a whole range of illnesses (including cancer and AIDS) for it depresses our immune systems. We can become seriously depressed, accident-prone, and suffer from pain for which there is apparently no physical cause. Back pain is particularly common among self-haters, not surprisingly since we just do not support ourselves (or allow ourselves to be supported) – and the function of the back is to support. It is probable that sometimes people put themselves in hospital as the only way they can give themselves the experience of being supported and cared for.

Often we are not aware of our own negativity and project it on to others. We can become paranoid, quick to take anger at imagined insults, and quite humourless. It is as if we are continually on the watch for confirmation of our own valuelessness. Everybody we meet is a potential judge, to be appeased before they accuse us of our shortcomings. Not surprisingly, our relationships suffer from our prickliness and depressiveness. And so does our work, for we will hardly show confidence, drive and outgoingness to our employers and customers – we just don't have the energy. We are also unlikely to be the easiest people to work with either.

In my experience self-hatred in varying degrees is very common. In the counselling situation it is usually the 'bottom line'. Behind the brash, aggressive, depressed or complaining client, eventually one uncovers the shrinking, vulnerable Child within, desperately lonely perhaps, or full of rage out of sheer frustration (see p 80). It is not surprising that so many people do not have a high opinion of themselves, for we have not been educated for it. Quite apart from whether our childhood was traumatic or loveless, we were taught not to be too 'full of ourselves', conceited, selfish, etc. Nobody in their right mind would think of telling others how good they were: it would be to court instant disapproval. Rather we should be modest, underplay our achievements and always put the other person first, for all the world as if we did not matter just as much as them.

And yet, as Louise Hay tells us from her vast experience as a healer, 'Happiness is feeling good about yourself'. Unless you feel good about yourself, you don't feel good, period. And, almost certainly, you won't feel good about anyone else either. Rather, you will be prey to negativity about them: jealousy, criticism, competitiveness – or downright paranoia. Jesus' admonition to 'Love thy neighbour as thyself' – no more, no less – is more than a pious ideal. It is a blueprint for physical, emotional and mental health.

How then to counteract the effects of conditioning and improve our self-image? Simply by being more aware of each occasion when we start to put ourselves down in our heads, to blame ourselves for something, to feel guilty, to compare ourselves unfavourably with others and generally give ourselves a bad time.

We act on what we believe to be true. If we tell ourselves often enough how bad we are, we will get to believe it – and express ourselves in the world in accordance with these tapes in the computers that are our brains. Fortunately, it is possible to cancel out these negative programmes and substitute positive programmes instead. These are called 'affirmations'. The best known one is 'Every day, in every way, I am getting better and better'. But affirmations can be used to generate more positive energy in our lives by cancelling out negative feelings about ourselves. And this is very important, for without a positive self-image our health, careers, relationships and capacity for enjoyment are all adversely affected. Depression *drains* energy – not only our own but that of the people around us as well. All that is needed is to repeat, as often as you wish (and certainly every time you catch yourself putting yourself down in your head) a positive statement about yourself. They may seem false at first, but this is only because you have formed bad habits. Keep at them, and by and by you will begin to feel better about yourself, to have more confidence and more energy.

To improve your self-image:

1 Immediately cancel out any harsh judgements that you catch yourself making about yourself.
2 Never invalidate yourself – or allow anybody else to invalidate you.
3 Reprogramme yourself with positive affirmations.

Everything is relative. As the Immortal Bard put it: 'Nothing is good nor bad, but thinking makes it so.' You can choose either to see yourself, for example, as a gentle and polite person, or a 'wet'; as a lively, high-energy person – or as too 'pushy'. The energy is what it is; the judgement, the interpretation, is yours. And Life is always ready to confirm whichever way we see ourselves, and provide experiences to match it. So choose to see yourself always in a positive light. Who is to say you are wrong? Remember that there is no objective thing called 'truth': it is all a question of interpretation. Remember the Ugly Duckling.

Here are some affirmations for you to try, to boost your confidence and optimism about yourself. At first you may feel awkward, disbelieving, phoney. This is only to be expected, for you are breaking a habit of self-invalidation. If you persevere, however, they will become a new reality for you and the sort of experiences you draw to yourself will change for the better.

Repeat them, preferably aloud, several times a day, and especially on awakening in the morning and just before dropping off to sleep at night. At these times you will be at your most relaxed and your subconscious will therefore be more receptive to new programming.

- I am an attractive person.
- People love me for who I am.
- I am efficient and creative in my work.
- I am totally lovable – just as I am.
- I love and approve of myself at all times.
- I am a magnificent, sensitive, loving and valuable human being.
- Being loved, happy and successful feels totally safe.
- There is no limit to how good I can feel.
- Everything I touch is a success.
- I now win all the time.
- I deserve the best of everything.

REACTION AND RESPONSE TO ANGER

Finally, a word or two about trying not to react automatically when somebody is expressing anger towards you. It is easy to do, for we usually feel quite threatened when we are on the receiving end of somebody's negativity, and instinctively try to defend ourselves. And so we polarise against each other and engage in verbal battle, which too often becomes a sort of ping-pong in which whoever scores the most points wins. This can be upsetting (especially if you are on the losing end!) and emotionally draining.

Sometimes, too, we may be surprised at how angry we get in return, at how much what the other person says affects us. This is because, in the jargon of therapy, they are 'pushing our buttons'. What this means is that all of us have unresolved tensions in our lives, psychological wounds and scars that cause us pain and fear when something happens to open them up again. Fritz Perls called them our 'unfinished business'. Somebody might be angry with us for some simple reason, justifiable or not. But if they are unconsciously pushing a button, the amount of energy that will be generated in us will either be quite out of proportion to the issue, or, after the row is over, we will go on dwelling on what happened and fret about it.

To the extent that we are aware of these vulnerable spots in our emotional make-up we will not be stampeded into reacting blindly and automatically every time they are activated. Much of our anger is from the past, past hurts and put-downs. They cloud our perception of what is really going on, make us read more into what is said than the other person meant.

Nobody ever can make you *feel* anything. They don't have that power, and to claim that they do is a manipulation and makes you a victim. You don't *have* to get angry just because the other person is angry. And if you do, remember that it is *your* anger, not theirs.

So don't leak energy every time there is some difference of opinion. Give yourself time to check out how you really feel about what is happening – and respond from that space. The old advice about counting to ten was very sound, and designed to achieve just this. Also, it helps if, instead of reacting to the other's behaviour or words, you try to feel the place they are coming from. Often you will intuit that they feel hurt, or threatened in some way. If you respond to that place, often this will defuse the situation and you will save a lot of energy. Remember, everybody has their 'buttons'.

MEDITATING ON THE OPPOSITE

The thing that is most important is not to brood over how awful everybody is and how badly they have treated you. This not only stops the negative energy from dispersing (as like all feelings, it will if you don't hang on to it and keep refuelling it), but means you will be stuck with it – to the detriment of your health and peace of mind.

Rather, help the bad feelings to dissolve by 'meditating on the opposite'. This simply means to forgive and forget – which is not the same as condoning whatever harm has been done to you. Wishing somebody harm creates karma which, soon or later, will come back to you. We always get back the type of energy we put out – multiplied. So wish them well, choose to see what happened as a learning experience, and, if you can, bring some humour to the situation.

There is a beautiful Buddhist meditation called Metta, which means 'loving kindness'. It consists simply of dwelling on loving thoughts, first towards yourself, then to the people close to you – and then to those for whom you feel some aversion. Include them all in your meditation – you will feel a whole lot better afterwards.

You could also take one of the Bach Flower Remedies. Take your pick, depending on which particular brand of negativity you are stuck in, from the following list. In Useful Addresses at the end of the book you can find out where to get them from. Fortunately, they are cheap. To quote from the official Dr Edward Bach Centre literature: 'As the Bach Remedies are benign in their action and can result in no unpleasant reactions, they can be taken by anyone.' Stock Concentrate Remedies will keep indefinitely – a 10ml size concentrate bottle will provide sufficient to make approximately 60 treatment bottles. More than one Remedy can be taken at the same time – two drops of each chosen Remedy in a cup of water and sipped at intervals, or in a 30ml (1fl oz) bottle filled with spring water (this represents a treatment bottle) from which four drops are taken directly on the tongue at least four times a day. The 'Rescue Remedy' is taken orally (four drops in water) but can also be applied externally either in liquid or in cream form. Dr Bach saved a fisherman's life in 1930 with this preparation.

The Bach Remedies

1 Agrimony

For those who suffer considerable inner torture which they try to dissemble behind a facade of cheerfulness.

2 Aspen

Apprehension – the feeling that something dreadful is going to happen without knowing why.

3 Beech

Critical and intolerant of others. Arrogant.

4 Centaury

Weakness of will; those who let themselves be exploited or imposed upon – who become subservient and have difficulty saying 'No'. Human doormat.

5 Cerato

Those who doubt their own judgement and seek advice of others. Often influenced and misguided.

6 Cherry Plum

Uncontrolled – irrational thoughts.

7 Chestnut Bud

Refusal to learn by experience; continual repetition of the same mistakes.

8 Chicory

The over-possessive who demands respect or attention (selfishness), and likes others to conform to their standards. Those who make martyrs of themselves.

9 Clematis

For those who are indifferent, inattentive, dreamy, absent-minded. Mental escapists from reality.

10 Crab Apple

A cleanser. For those feeling unclean or ashamed of ailments. Self-disgust/ hatred. Houseproud.

11 Elm

For temporary feelings of inadequacy; those overwhelmed by responsibilities. Normally very capable.

12 Gentian

Despondent. Easily discouraged and dejected.

13 Gorse

For despair and hopelessness; utter despondency – 'What's the use?'.

14 Heather

People who are obsessed with their own troubles and experiences. Talkative 'bores' – poor listeners.

15 Holly

For those who are jealous, envious, vengeful and suspicious. And those who hate.

16 Honeysuckle

For those with nostalgia and who constantly dwell in the past. Homesickness.

17 Hornbeam

'Monday morning feeling' but once started, the task is usually fulfilled. Procrastination.

18 Impatiens

Impatience, irritability.

19 Larch

Despondency due to lack of self-confidence; expectation of failure, so fails to make the attempt. Feels inferior, though has the ability.

20 Mimulus

The fear of known things. Shyness, timidity.

21 Mustard

Deep gloom or depression that descends for no known cause and lifts just as suddenly. Melancholy.

22 Oak

Brave determined types who struggle on against adversity despite setbacks. Plodders.

23 Olive

Drained of energy – everything an effort. Fatigued.

24 Pine

Feelings of guilt. Blames self for the mistakes of others. Feels unworthy.

25 Red Chestnut

Over care and excessive concern for others, especially those held dear.

26 Rock Rose

Alarmed, scared, panicky, full of trepidation.

27 Rock Water

For those who are hard on themselves – who often overwork. Rigid minded, self-denying.

28 Scleranthus

Uncertainty/indecision/vacillation. Fluctuating moods.

29 Star of Bethlehem

For all the effects of serious news, or fright following an accident etc.

30 Sweet Chestnut

Absolute dejection.

31 Vervain

Over-enthusiasm, over-effort; straining. Fanatical and highly-strung. Incensed and frustrated by injustices.

32 Vine

Dominating/inflexible/ambitious/tyrannical/autocratic. Arrogant pride. Considered to be good leaders.

33 Walnut

Protection remedy from powerful influences – helps adjustment to any transition or change eg puberty, menopause, divorce, new surroundings.

34 Water Violet

Proud, reserved, sedate types, sometimes 'superior'. Little emotional involvement but reliable/dependable.

35 White Chestnut

For those with persistent unwanted thoughts. Preoccupations with some worry or episode. Mental arguments.

36 Wild Oat

Helps to determine one's intended path in life.

37 Wild Rose

Resignation, apathy. Drifters who accept their lot, making little effort for improvement – lacking ambition.

38 Willow

Resentment and bitterness with 'not fair' and 'poor me' attitude.

39 Rescue Remedy

A combination of Cherry Plum, Clematis, Impatiens, Rock Rose and Star of Bethlehem. All-purpose emergency composite for shock, terror, panic, emotional upsets, 'stage fright', examination, dentistry etc. Can also be externally applied to burns, bites, sprains and so on. Comforting, calming and reassuring to those distressed by startling experiences.

6
ENERGY IN RELATIONSHIPS

Relating to people is always an exchange of energy. Think about how you feel after relating to some people. Do you ever feel:

- fatigued?
- depressed?
- inadequate?
- guilty?

If so, you have allowed the other person to drain you. We can emerge from an interaction with more energy than we had before, or less. We put out energy to each other, not only by what we actually say, but also in more subtle ways — our tone of voice, facial expression, the way we look at them, and even by what we are thinking to ourselves. Often for some reason we cannot pin down, we can sense that the other person perhaps does not like us, or is not to be trusted. Ultimately we relate to each other at a vibrational level. As Martial put it in one of his epigrams 2000 years ago:

> *I do not like thee Doctor Fell,*
> *The reason why I cannot tell:*
> *But this alone I know full well,*
> *I do not like thee Doctor Fell.*

And it has nothing to do with words: How can I hear what you are saying when what you *are* is shouting in my ears?

If we ourselves are coming from a place of love and optimism, the other will sense it. We will part more charged with energy, feeling good about ourselves and somehow nourished.

But it also can work the other way. If you are with somebody who only wants to complain, blame and tell you how hard life is, how terrible people are, you might well be caught up in playing what Eric Berne, the founder of Transactional Analysis, classified as the game of 'Ain't It Awful' and be brought down by them if you are not aware of what is happening. The worst thing you can do is to try and solve their problems for them. If you do, one of two things is likely to happen. Either they will listen eagerly and suck energy – and continue after they have left you according to their old negative pattern. Or, they will counter any suggestion you make by playing 'Yes, But . . .' until you give up defeated, baffled – and drained. In which case the game has developed into the game (deeply satisfying for victims) of 'Now I've Got You, You Sonofabitch'.

So never try to solve anybody's problems for them. Often their real problem is that they want attention or that they manipulate others by playing helpless. You are not doing them a favour by colluding with their victim-consciousness. Rather, if you really feel you want to help them:

1 Just listen.
2 Ask 'What exactly are you feeling right now?'
3 Ask 'What are *you* going to do about it?'

The best thing one can do for anybody (and this is the goal of therapy) is to *empower* them, to encourage them to come up with their own creative solutions to the problems we all have in our lives. Don't get 'hooked' into trying to do it for them. It never works.

Relationships can be heaven or they can be hell, nourishing or toxic. Nothing makes our work suffer more than when things are going badly at home. We find it hard to concentrate, feel miserable and shrink when the working day is over at having to go back for another round of verbal battling, nagging and misunderstanding. Some relationships, of course, are irreparably damaged, and maybe the best thing you can do for each other is to finish it. But very often, if love has not completely died, they can be repaired, but only by bringing more awareness and understanding to what is *really* happening between you. Love, alas, is not enough. Here, then, are some dynamics that operate in pretty well all relationships. *Tout comprendre, c'est tout pardonner* – hopefully.

TOGETHERNESS V. SPACE

A recurring dynamic in relationships, and one that is probably the cause of more friction than any other factor, is that of the polarity between wanting more intimacy, and needing more space, physical or psychological. One of the concepts in Gestalt is that of the 'contact boundary' which everybody has. This boundary between us and other people expands and contracts. Sometimes we will be feeling expansive and be needing more closeness, more communication, more 'togetherness'. Yet at others, especially if we are tired or have something on our minds, it is just the opposite. We may need to be alone, with time to ourselves to think, or to read, to listen to music, or just to relax without having to keep a conversation together. At these times attempts of another to come close or to engage us in conversation is experienced as an intrusion – which in fact it is, since they are penetrating our contact boundary.

The problem is therefore insensitivity to one another's spaces. With an understanding partner there may be no big problem. The problem arises if the 'expanded' partner needs attention and is prepared to manipulate to get it. Signs that this is happening are remarks like 'I can't say a thing without you jumping down my throat', or 'I don't know what's come over you these days' – or some other expression of the 'Poor Me' game. More statements designed to produce guilt are 'Is it something I said?' and (the big guns) 'You don't love me any more' (which may or may not be accompanied by tears). Sulking, too, is a popular one.

Once again, don't allow yourself to be manipulated. You have a right to enjoy your own space once in a while without feeling guilty about it. It can be taken gracefully and non-aggressively (unless, of course, you do feel guilty that you are not totally available all the time). And if you do give in you will only resent it. Better to give yourself permission to be alone for a while, so that when you come back to relating you will be totally there – and enjoy it. What we tend to do out of politeness, however, is to dither somewhere in the middle, which is not very satisfying for anybody.

ALONENESS AND DEPENDENCE

A lot of the clinging and constant need for attention and validation that bedevils many relationships springs from one or other of the partners' fear of being alone, of being abandoned, and is also very much to do with low self-esteem. So they become over-dependent, gradually losing touch with their own needs and identity because they are so anxious to appease their partner and meet expectations. All of us will have seen relationships where one partner has ended up as a mere shadow of the other. This in fact can backfire and ultimately threaten the relationship, for it breeds boredom in one and secret resentment in the other – and fury and recrimination when their expectations are not met ('After all I have done/given up for you . . .').

To ask for what you need, to say what you want, to have differences of opinion are healthy for a relationship. Don't expect your partner to satisfy all your needs: it is not possible for one person to do this. Don't expect the other person to make you happy, either. It is *your* job to do this, and as we suggested earlier, nobody has the power to make us *feel* anything. If a relationship is not to become a prison one must keep one's inner freedom and continue to take responsibility for oneself.

Learn to enjoy aloneness as well as intimacy. Don't confuse aloneness with loneliness – they are two quite separate things. Loneliness is the absence of the other, whereas aloneness is the presence of oneself. And it can be blissful, quite apart from allowing your energy to build up. In fact, the best way I know of recharging batteries is to be alone for a while, and in silence. It is the basis of all relaxation and meditation techniques. And, ultimately, what is a relationship anyway but two alonenesses meeting?

SUBPERSONALITIES

Relationships are mirrors in which we see ourselves reflected, or rather, our *selves*, of which we have many. Our moods change all the time, according to which one of these selves has been activated and takes centre stage. Here are some of the selves (or, as they are called in psychotherapy, subpersonalities) that everybody has. They are really different *energies*, but they do indeed behave like real people inside us.

The Child

There is a Child in all of us, though many people keep it well hidden. The Child represents our vulnerability (which is why people hide it) and capacity to feel and to be playful. It needs above all to be loved and reassured and to feel safe. Like all young children, however, it is not very articulate and cannot always say what it needs. To protect our vulnerability (and to keep out of trouble) we all, in the process of growing up, developed another subpersonality . . .

The Controller

The Controller is the introjected authority figures of your youth — parents, teachers, priests and so on. We have made their rules, their values our own and feel guilty when we do not live by them. It is in fact like a Parent inside us, making sure we do not 'go over the top' and behave badly. If we do, it can be quite punitive. The Controller has very definite ideas as to what is right and what is wrong. It is rigid and judgemental of others, and any perceived threat to the Child that it is its function to protect brings out its wrath.

The Pleaser

The Pleaser is the part of us that will do anything in order to be liked. It cannot bear criticism in any form, and is quick to appease, to disarm with charm. It does, in fact, want to be loved by everybody. We had a long training in pleasing when we were young: much of our education consisted in pleasing our teachers. Later on, it was our employers, our girlfriends, our men. We learned many tricks to be popular — and if none of them happen to work we are in despair, for our whole self-image is bound up with what others think of us.

The 'Pusher'

The Pusher is the one that never stops trying to make us *more*: more rich, more successful, more beautiful, more powerful . . . It is the subpersonality whose driving energy fuels all workaholism, and makes us sign up for self-improvement courses, punish our bodies in the search for perfection. It is, once again, the introjection of all those school reports ('Must work harder') and parental urgings to 'get on' in the world. It has two allies in our psychological make-up: the **Perfectionist** and the **Critic**. Between them these three parts of us can drive us mad (or make us ill) because they are always 'on our backs', demanding more and more effort to succeed in reaching their impossibly high standards. And we are never good enough . . . The inner

Critic, particularly, is the voice in our heads that is always judging us
– and finding us wanting. It is responsible for low self-esteem, continually comparing ourselves unfavourably with others, depression
and, sometimes, even suicide.

There are many more subpersonalities that are specific to certain
people: for example, the untidy one that seems to need to create chaos
around him or her; the one who is always late; the one who is terrified
of committing themselves to anything or taking responsibility . . .
These, too, can drive us to distraction.

To the extent that we are aware of each other's subpersonalities
and how predictably and automatically they make us behave, we can
control them and save being taken over by them and reacting robot-
fashion, whenever they are activated. We don't have to act out everything we feel. And we may even be able to bring some humour to our
quarrels by making the other aware that he or she is into their
Pleaser, Pusher, Controller etc. Above all, we can look into the place
the other is really coming from rather than reacting to their words or
behaviour. Very often, when they are laying down the law and they
are quite awful, it is their threatened Child that their Controller will
be trying to protect. To realise this is immediately to step out of the
struggle of rival Controllers to dominate the other and to allow us to
address the Child directly. When the Child feels seen and heard the
fight goes out of the Controller. It is not needed any more.

POLARISATION

Without such awareness, what often happens in quarrels is that
subpersonalities polarise against each other. A common example of
such polarisation is that of Parent (ie Controller) – Child. Here is
how it works.

Anne has lost much of her confidence. She does not seem to be able
to make any decisions without agonising over them, and is desperately afraid that she may be wrong when she does.

Her parents were strict and sent her to a boarding school run by
a particularly authoritarian religious order. She married a man
who was dynamic and confident, who subconsciously she felt
would be strong enough to look after her. This in fact he did,
materially and otherwise. As the relationship progressed, Anne

became more and more dependent on her husband, leaving all major decisions to him. He was quite happy with this, as he liked to be in charge.

As he became more and more entrenched in his Controller, however, and became more and more dogmatic, Anne became increasingly more identified with her Child and her Pleaser. It was like being back at school again. Her Child felt safe enough, but the other parts of her personality were not given any chance to surface. She therefore gave herself no chance to express her creativity – or her playfulness. She wonders why she feels depressed a lot of the time and sort of trapped. She also fears that her husband is becoming bored with her. This could well be because she no longer has very much to say to him. She feels uninteresting, stale, flat.

Anne is naturally introverted. If she had been more extroverted it could have gone the other way, and the polarisation could well have become that of Controlling Parent/Rebellious Daughter, in which case there would be a lot of quarrelling as she projected on him all the authority figures from her childhood – and then rebelled against them. She would be on the lookout for anything her man did that could possibly be interpreted as an attempt to limit her freedom. She'd be argumentative, self-assertive and disagreeing almost for the hell of it.

Unless the partners have some insight into what is happening they will be locked in this struggle (him for control, her for survival) till kingdom come. That is, unless they decide to end the relationship. But this will not change very much. Unless the pattern is changed, they will go on repeating it in other relationships as well. The essence of subpersonalities is that they are recurring *automatic* ways of behaving.

DISOWNED ENERGIES

What tends to happen also in relationships is that a subpersonality disowned and unacknowledged in one partner tends to be projected on to the other. A partner, for example, who, without daring to acknowledge it, hankers deep down after an extra-marital adventure will tend to be jealous and to misjudge the most innocent social interactions of the other.

Energy, as we have said before, cannot be destroyed. It can only be transformed through awareness and understanding. Otherwise, if we remain unconscious of the parts within us, we will merely project them outwards on others. This is the basis of paranoia and harsh judgements. And the more terrified we are of the Caliban within all of us (Jung called it the 'Shadow'), and disown it, the harsher our judgements will be.

And the other will be forced to carry, albeit without realising it, the energy we are repressing, and to act it out for us.

PSYCHOLOGICAL TYPES

The energy that, willy nilly, partners carry for each other may not be a subpersonality, but an underdeveloped mode of being. Jung postulated that there are four basic psychological types who see the world and respond to it in different ways. These four types are:

- Thinking types.
- Feeling types.
- Sensing types.
- Intuitive types.

What this means is that the way we perceive reality is different for different people, and our values also are different. This can cause misunderstanding in relating, for two people may in fact be talking a different type of language. Thinking and feeling types, for example, are opposite: the logical person will tend to be frustrated and baffled by the 'emotional thinking' of the feeling type, who will probably in turn accuse the thinking type of being always 'in his head' (it is usually a man) and of being cold and unfeeling. Similarly, sensing and intuitive types are opposite: the earthiness of the sensing type will be repugnant to the finer sensibilities of the intuitive, while the senser will get easily irritated by the lack of practicality of the intuitive.

We rely on one or two of these four modes to get us through life. The others remain latent in us, only a potential, unless we work on ourselves to develop them. Even so, they will never be as paramount as our primary type. How this affects relating is not simply that we can misunderstand each other because we are unaware of our differing values and modes of perception, but also because we may gradually start to carry the undeveloped energy for the other. In our culture it is rather the men who are conditioned to be logical and practical (ie thinking and sensing) and to leave feeling and intuition to their mates.

GETTING HIGH TOGETHER

I have an old friend whom I may not see for years on end (he is a therapist practising in California), yet on the rare occasions we do meet up again we always get high together – and I don't mean on marijuana (though a bottle or two of wine over dinner probably helps). We will talk and talk until the small hours of the morning, catching up on what has been happening in our lives. The energy we generate is always a nourishing and expanding experience and I have often wondered what the dynamic is between us. I have come to the following conclusions that I suspect apply in all social interactions.

1 Listen with full attention when the other is speaking.
2 Make eye contact.
3 Be willing to share the other person's spaces – even if you don't agree with or understand them.
4 Never contradict – it produces immediate contraction in the other.

What makes us expand are the feelings of:

- Freedom to say whatever we like without being judged.
- Being *heard* by the other person.
- Playfulness and humour.
- The other being interested in what we are saying.

Try it out for yourself. Allow the person you are relating to lots of freedom to sing their song. Listen attentively, ignoring any judgements that may be running through your head. Never contradict. Try to understand where they are coming from – then share with them what is going on with you. Don't get caught up in a clash of ideas or in polarisation. Rather share *feelings*. Always say something positive, for negativity contracts, and you can actually *feel* the loving vibration in the room being dampened by a pessimistic remark or criticism of others.

This way of interacting is called 'laddering': it is like helping each other to get higher by taking it in turns to put out positive and loving energy into the room. As you help each other to expand in this way any worries you may have had recede and life feels totally worthwhile, exciting and *fun*. All that is needed is goodwill and awareness of what sort of energy you are offloading on to the other person and bringing into the room.

SEXUAL ENERGY

Sexual energy sometimes seems to be doing its own thing regardless of our best intentions. We can be attracted to the most unsuitable people, sometimes fail, embarrassingly to 'deliver the goods' on request, feel sexy at totally inappropriate moments, or do things that in retrospect make us blush. Sex can be the occasion of the highest bliss – or the deepest misery. Many people go through life quite baffled as to how to handle it.

Somebody once said that all you need to know about sex is 'When you're hot, you're hot. When you're not, you're not'. This is a useful way of looking at sex, for it means that we don't allow ourselves to become obsessed with it, be controlled by it, or brought down by it.

Our sexual energy is an expression of who we are. The more relaxed we are with it, the more we enjoy it, the less our anxiety and tension about it, the easier it flows. There are many things that can get in the way of sexual energy and expression. High on the list is the fact that usually our image of ourselves is very much involved – and that makes us tense. Men, particularly, have been conditioned to equate their masculinity with their sexual performance. This means that, whatever else a sexual encounter may mean for them, it always carries the pressure to 'prove oneself' – which is hardly conducive to relaxing into it.

Women, too, can be confused by their own sexual identity. For centuries the archetypes of the Virgin, the Mother and the Whore have struggled in their Unconscious for dominance. One of the most liberating aspects of Women's Lib has been to encourage new possibilities, notably of the sexually free woman and the strong, economically independent woman. (The archetypes for these are Aphrodite and Athena.) It is probably true to say that nowadays it is more the men who need liberating than women, and not least from the straitjacket of 'machismo'. For to be satisfying at more than a purely physical level a love relationship needs the ability (and willingness) to share feelings (including vulnerability and tenderness) as well as commitment – things that scare the pants off many men.

If you feel that your interest in sex is drying up it may well be that you are low on energy generally. You may need to improve your health, stop working long hours, get more exercise, take in more protein and vitamins, vitamin E and ginseng particularly. But often the problem (if it is a problem) is more psychological than physical. It helps to take stock of where you are 'at' with sex from the point of view of your (probably subconscious) attitudes, expectations and desires. To help you do this counselling or short-term psychotherapy could be worthwhile.

Our bodies never lie. If your sex energy is dwindling you should ask yourself the question 'Do I *really* want sex right now?' And there may be perfectly valid reasons why not. It may be that you are fatigued, bored, subconsciously resenting your partner, or more intent on meeting their expectations than pleasing yourself and having a good time (in which case you will probably end up resenting them even more). Until you clear these 'hidden agendas' they will block your energy from flowing.

Habit, too, is a passion-killer. Try being more imaginative when you make love. Bring a little fantasy to it. Remember, it's not meant to be serious. It's meant to be *fun*. Allow yourself to be more playful. Be aware of your own expectations about how it should go – and let go of them. For example, neither of you *has* to have an orgasm every time you make love, or, indeed, to have sex when what you really need is to have a good cuddle. The most important thing is to keep loving energy flowing between you – and that means during the day as well as in bed. The sexual energy will take care of itself.

However you do it, get out of a rut. A well-tried way of restoring romance to tired relationships is to take a holiday together and leave the pressures and stress behind, preferably to somewhere where you can laze in the sun together, play in the sea, and dress up for dinner under the stars. You'll feel more alive, as well as looking better with a suntan. And knowing you look good will also make you feel more confident in your own attractiveness.

Finally, never assume you are too old to enjoy sex. You can be too young, but never too old – unless you think you are.

7

CONSERVING KI

According to ancient eastern philosophy, our basic constitution is determined by our pre-natal 'ki' (energy, life force). How much or how little ki we are born with depends on factors like the age and health of our parents, the circumstances of our birth etc. This store of ki can never be increased, but it can be diminished by excess of any form, for example, too many late nights, overwork, abuse of alcohol and drugs, and sexual excess. It can also be conserved through a moderate and healthy life-style, above all good diet, deep breathing, exercise and positive attitudes. We can burn ourselves out by being too busy. It has been suggested that this was the reason for Bruce Lee's premature death: the phenomenal energy he used in his pictures eventually became used up.

If you will pardon the pun, moderation is the key to conserving ki. Excessive emotion (including even *joy*), for example, disturbs the ki in the heart region – with consequent danger of heart attacks and depressed immunity (since the thymus which controls immunity is situated in this region). Grief affects the lungs and the skin, while anger (especially if it solidifies into chronic irritation) can cause headaches and problems in the organs associated with digestion. Fear, similarly, causes ki energy to descend to the lower abdomen, which is why we may experience the need to urinate or defaecate when we are very frightened. Overwork of any kind stresses the adrenals, situated over the kidneys. Ki is considered to be stored in the kidneys, where it is referred to as 'kidney jing'. This store can be used up, not only by workaholism, but also by excessive sexual ejaculations – though what this will be varies from person to person. The oriental view is that the acceptable frequency varies with the seasons. In spring, for example, it is suggested that two or three ejaculations a week does no harm, less in summer and autumn. In winter, however, oriental physicians recommend that there should be no ejaculations at all. This will probably be an alarming thought to all but natural celibates. But one has to remember that in the East the practice of sexual intercourse without ejaculation is considered to promote not only greater vitality but also higher consciousness (as, for example, in *tantra yoga*).

We are also enjoined to take care during extremes of weather and not to expose ourselves to wind, excessive heat, dampness and cold. Regarding food, it should not be too hot, spicy or cold, for example, eaten or drunk straight from the fridge. We are, in other words, to avoid excesses of yang and yin which will cause imbalance to our ki, which otherwise will manifest in symptoms like restlessness, excitability and insomnia (excess of yang) or fatigue, chilliness or poor circulation (excess of yin).

ABORTING SYMPTOMS

The viewpoint of holistic health is that illness is always the outward sign of inner disharmony. Sickness or health is a function of the state of our *energy*, whether it is plentiful or depleted, balanced and flowing or stagnating and blocked. It was the pioneer of research into stress, Sir Hans Selye, who first among 'orthodox' practitioners of health became interested in the fact that, before overt symptoms of illness become manifest, they are always preceded by a diffused feeling of 'unwellness' – depression, fatigue, digestive upsets and the like. More recently, Dr Peter Nixon, a consultant in cardiology at Charing Cross Hospital in London, together with Dr David Peters, a general practitioner, have been stressing the importance of directing attention to these bodily symptoms of distress while we are still in this nether land between 'not feeling well' and the manifestation of full-blown symptoms in the body.

If one is sufficiently aware of one's energy levels, one can feel when one is 'going down with something', a cold, for example, or influenza. And if one acts immediately to replenish one's energy, very often the bodily symptoms can be aborted before they take hold. The most important things to do when you sense that all is not well are to:

● Down tools and rest. Allow your energy to accumulate again.
● Practise deep alpha relaxation several times a day.

- Cut out stress in any form. Take it easy for a while.
- Take nourishing, easily digested food. Soups are particularly good.
- Step up your intake of vitamins – especially high-dose vitamin C.
- Drink a lot of filtered water and fruit juices.

Most times this will work to restore your energy to an even keel. If it doesn't, that suggests to me that right now you *need* to be ill. The reason could be that your body needs to discharge toxins, or that you need to give yourself the space to regroup your psychic energies or to adjust to major changes that may be happening in your life, or simply that it is the only way your Child can experience being cared for and not having to shoulder responsibilities for a while.

ACUPUNCTURE

Where the so-called 'alternative therapies' score over allopathic medicine is that they are more geared to dealing with these non-specific symptoms of energy imbalance, whereas a doctor will very likely tell the patient that there is nothing wrong with them if the results of tests show nothing pathological. It is estimated, for example, that about three-quarters of patients crowding the consulting-rooms of GPs are suffering from fatigue and stress, about which their doctor can do very little. And yet these are the two things that more than anything else lead to illness if unchecked.

This is not to disparage the very real achievements of modern medicine – one thanks God for the discovery of antibiotics, for example. And the 'alternative therapist' is much less able to cope with acute crises (appendicitis, for example) than the surgeon – though it must be added that in the great cholera epidemics of the last century the record of homeopathy proved to be in fact better than that of allopathic treatment of the victims.

But for prophylaxis – for avoiding disease by having their energy balanced from time to time – more and more people since the 1960s have had recourse to an acupuncturist or homeopath either routinely, or when they feel 'under the weather'. The acupuncturist works with tiny needles (don't worry, they don't hurt!) and *moxa* on points along the energy meridians which we show on pages 93–95. Moxa involves lighting little cones of mugwort over a point on a meridian, and extinguishing it just before it touches the skin. (The representation of the course of the meridians, and the pressure points along them is approximate.) The session will be preceded by the acupuncturist assessing exactly where the patient's imbalance lies, by taking the pulses (there are twelve of them), checking the tongue and – especially in the first session – asking lots of questions about tastes, life-style preferences etc. At the very least, one comes away from an acupuncture session feeling seen, which may or may not be the case with your GP since they have so little time to devote to each patient. At best he or she will treat your physical symptoms rather than *you*, whereas the holistic approach is to treat the whole patient. If this is done successfully, symptoms (the manifestation, not the cause, of dis-ease) will automatically abate as imbalances are corrected.

ENERGY MERIDIANS

These are the channels through which ki flows throughout the body. There are 14 of them (see the following pages for 11 of these). Some of the meridians are yin, some are yang. They are thought to have been formed when mankind was still running on all fours. The direction of energy flow in yin meridians runs up the inside and front of the body, which would have been closest to the earth, while the yang energy flow is down the back and outside surfaces which would have been exposed to sunlight.

Each meridian is associated with a particular organ or psycho-physical function, but in fact its influence extends beyond the organ itself. This means that if we are having trouble with the liver meridian, for example, it is not necessarily the liver itself that is in a bad state, but our liver *energy*. Along the length of each meridian there are points which, if stimulated by needles or thumb pressure, affect the flow of ki throughout the length of the meridian. This is what is done in acupuncture or acupressure/shiatsu. (See pages 97 and 98.)

At a symposium held by the World Health Organisation in Peking in 1979, medical acupuncturists from all over the world compiled a list of conditions that they claimed could be cured or improved by acupuncture. There were more than 40 of these. They included disorders of the respiratory and digestive systems (including asthma and bronchitis, constipation, diarrhoea, and duodenal ulcers) as well as nervous disorders, migraine and the relief of pain.

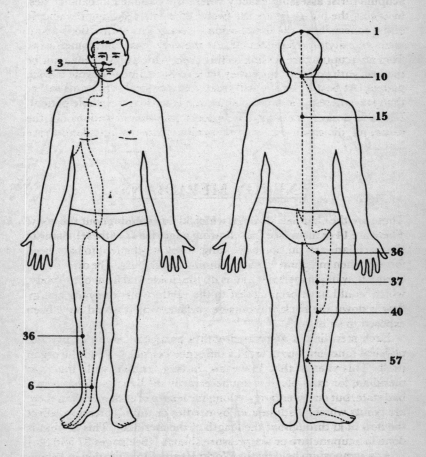

Fig 5   *Stomach Meridian 3, 4, 36*   **Fig 6**   *Bladder Meridian 1, 10, 15,*
            Spleen Meridian 6   *36, 37, 40, 57*

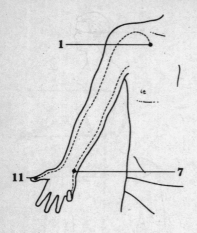

Fig 7   *Lung Meridian 1, 11*
          Heart Meridian 7

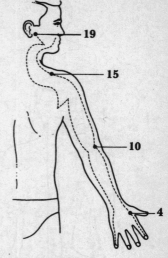

Fig 8   *Large Intestine Meridian 4, 10, 15*
          Small Intestine Meridian 19

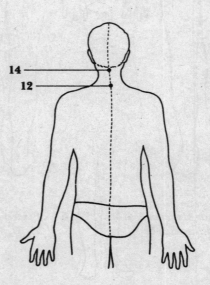

Fig 9   *Governing Vessel Meridian 12, 14*

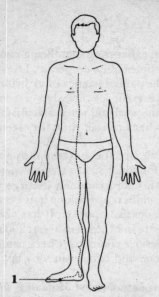

Fig 10 *Kidney Meridian 1*   **Fig 11** *Gall Bladder Meridian 20*

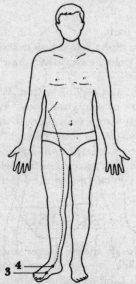

Fig 12 *Liver Meridian 3, 4*

HANDLING PAIN

There are few things more wearing and exhausting than being constantly in pain. We lose sleep, feel sometimes quite desperate. I have seen people I love reduced to tears by the pain of sciatica or arthritis. One feels quite helpless. And why, I ask myself, does one always seem to get an abscessed tooth flaring up at the weekend when a dentist is unavailable? The nights are the worst when one is in pain: they seem endless and one feels totally alone.

Assuming that your doctor has investigated the source of the pain and has done as much as he or she can for you, you are on your own. Acupuncture could well help. It is used in China routinely in surgery instead of anaesthetics. By 1979 three million operations had been performed using acupuncture, with no deaths reported. It has also been used in Germany at the Heart Centre in Munich in about 2000. In Britain too, many National Health Service clinics have been using acupuncture with patients with migraine and back pain who have not responded to drugs or surgery.

We can to some extent lessen the sharpness of pain by relaxing, for tension makes us contract and tighten our muscles. The following tips might help:

- Breathing into the pain.
- Practising the deep alpha relaxation described in chapter 3.
- Trying to feel the pain more rather than fighting it. Resistance makes us more tense.
- Visualising the pain and staying with it. What colour is it? Where exactly is the centre of it in your body? What shape is it? What texture is it? As you watch your pain, it will change its form and colour. If you stay with it long enough, it should diminish in intensity, and sometimes (especially in the case of headaches) disappear completely. The exception to this is toothache – you're stuck with it until you can get to the dentist.

SHIATSU

In Japanese the word *shi* means finger and *atsu* means pressure. Acupressure is another name for this oriental system of massage in which fingers, thumbs (and sometimes elbows and feet) are pressed on to certain points along the meridians called *tsubos*. There are 361 of these points, but in practice only 92 are used. The number of points along meridians varies. The Heart Meridian for example has only nine, whereas the Bladder Meridian has 67.

To treat oneself to a shiatsu massage is to stimulate energy flow along the meridians to ease tension, fatigue, pain and symptoms of disease. The Shiatsu Society publishes a newsletter and can supply a list of practitioners and teachers in Britain (see Useful Addresses).

Remember that where one experiences the actual pain or discomfort is not necessarily the point that has to be worked on: this may be further along the meridian line. Shiatsu is most useful for prophylaxis, for maintaining our vitality and stamina by preventing energy from getting blocked in the first place. It is obviously better to get a shiatsu expert to massage you, but there are still points that one can work on by oneself. Use thumbs to press on the point for seven to ten seconds, and repeat on the corresponding point on the other side of the body. You will know when you have found the point as you will feel a slight indentation and feel a twinge.

Here are some of the points you can try, with the conditions that they ameliorate. The points are numbered on the meridian charts on pages 93–95.

Stomach Meridian

3: sinus trouble, tension
4: toothache, tension
36: tired legs, general wellbeing

Spleen Meridian

6: menstrual pain, obesity, insomnia

Bladder Meridian

The longest of all the meridians, starting in the face and ending in the feet.

1: eyestrain
10: headache
15: irritability
36: sciatica, lower back pain
37: sciatica, tired legs
40: sciatica, lower back pain, calf cramps
57: sciatica, muscle cramps, tired legs

Lung Meridian

1: colds, cough, asthma
11: sore throat, coughs

Heart Meridian

7: irritability, insomnia, constipation

Large Intestine Meridian

4: diarrhoea, toothache, general wellbeing
10: sore legs, fatigue in arms, general wellbeing
15: shoulder joint pain, frozen shoulder

Small Intestine Meridian

19: ringing in the ears

Governing Vessel Meridian

12: asthma, colds
14: allergies, asthma, headaches, colds

Kidney Meridian

1: menstrual pain

Gall Bladder Meridian

20: colds, headaches

Liver Meridian

3: headaches
4: arthritis in the ankles, lower back pain

T'AI CHI

Tuning into ki (chi in Chinese) and flowing with it is very much the oriental way of harmonising our body and mind energy that protects us from the dis-ease that is the result of disharmony. It has been described as 'meditation in motion'. Originally one of the martial arts, t'ai chi evolved into a system of ritualised movements in slow motion that have the effect of grounding, centring, relaxing and focussing concentration. Each of the movements has to be performed with total concentration, which has the effect of slowing down the mind. There are two forms, one with over 100 movements (taking about 20 minutes to work through) and the short form with 37 movements (taking about ten minutes).

It is virtually impossible to describe t'ai chi in words: the only way really is to see it being performed, as one sometimes does in city parks. In China it is a common occurrence to see whole groups of people of all ages practising together early in the morning. It is both weird and graceful and has a calming effect even on the observer. Some cardiologists have in fact prescribed t'ai chi for patients with heart trouble, hypertension or angina, for it is a form of exercise that imposes no strain. It is also ideal for workaholics and those who drive themselves too hard as a prophylactic against coronaries. One needs a teacher for t'ai chi: if you want to learn it the simplest way is to contact the British T'ai Chi Chuan Association (see Useful Addresses).

AIKIDO

A martial art from Japan that is becoming increasingly popular in the West, aikido seeks to promote flowing with ki energy, like t'ai chi but in association with a partner. It is the art of non-resistance *par excellence* and surrendering to the energy of one's opponent rather than trying to control and fight it.

Classes are usually for 20 or so people in the *dojo* or practice room. There is a formality about procedure and etiquette that is typically Japanese. Classes start with a short period of meditation, followed by limbering up exercises. Partners then work together on movements first demonstrated by the teacher. The basic theme is non-resistance: you use your partner's own energy to bring them down. You go with it when pulled, turn away when pushed. Winning or losing is not as important as remaining centred, balanced and flowing.

The benefits claimed for aikido, apart from enhancing physical fitness and suppleness, are increased confidence and sense of well-being. Most important, perhaps, are that one becomes more aware of and 'tuned in' to ki so that one is not only aware of when one is leaking energy, but can actually anticipate partners' moves in advance.

The British Aikido Federation (see Useful Addresses) can supply a list of teachers.

POSTURAL THERAPIES

The West has also developed its own approaches to promoting the free flow of energy. Much of the theory of these is based on Wilhelm Reich's theory of *bioenergy* which is basically the same as ki. This energy can be trapped in the muscles as a result of holding tension over the years and repressed feelings. An interesting concept is that the process of repression of energy produces protective 'armouring' in our bodies, which, as Reich put it in his book *The Sexual Revolution*, results inevitably 'in a limitation of the total ability to live'. Most of us, as a result of our conditioning, have produced this armouring, which affects our posture and can be seen most noticeably in the 'mask' we have all learned to wear. Alexander Lowen worked out a system of 'stress positions' (which he called bioenergetics) which allow this energy to be released, often accompanied by catharsis of these repressed feelings, anger, fear, grief etc.

In America too, rolfing was developed by Ida Rolf in the 1960s to break through this armouring and release the buried emotions and traumas that first produced them. A rolfing treatment consists of ten sessions in which the therapist works on the connective tissues of the body, stretching and separating out the layers of tissue. If this sounds painful, it is. It is also usually very cathartic. The Rolf Institute is based in the United States (see Useful Addresses).

Much more subtle is the Alexander Technique, named after its founder, an Australian who was formerly an actor. Alexander's career was threatened when he kept losing his voice during performances, and he set out to find out why. He came to the conclusion that the cause was his bad posture: that he was pulling his head backwards and downwards during his performances. He concluded that, in order to function efficiently, we have to stop doing what comes naturally after years of bad postural habits. 'We must,' he said, 'appreciate the part played by an improving manner of use in the restoration and maintenance of psycho-physical efficiency and conditions of wellbeing.' He taught that mind and body were related, that there are 'right' postures for health and wellbeing – and wrong ones. The Alexander teacher seeks through a series of 'lessons' to re-educate the student into doing what at first will feel unnatural, but what is in fact the way they *should* be moving and hold themselves for energy to flow freely. A directory of all recognised teachers in Britain can be obtained from the Society of Teachers of the Alexander Technique (see Useful Addresses).

PSYCHOLOGICAL THERAPIES

Since mind and body are not separate systems but part of a continuum, it follows that our energy can be changed not only through the postural therapies described above, but also through alteration of consciousness. We are 'body-minds' and any changes we make in the way we *think* will automatically be registered in the way we *feel*, in other words in the quality of our energy.

There are many therapies which aim to produce a change in attitudes and awareness, with resultant improvement in quality of life. The best known is counselling – a misnomer, because the good counsellor is not one who tries to give advice and solve our problems for us, but aims instead to empower the client to make new choices as a result of insight into his or her self-destructive patterns. Such counselling can be either short-term (eg a few weeks) or long-term (eg a few years), the latter being expensive if one is, for example, in Jungian analysis.

Over the last 20 years or so, humanistic psychology has developed a variety of approaches to developing insight and awareness into what we do and how we do it, or, to use the jargon, 'why our lives are not working'. They include encounter groups, Gestalt therapy, transactional analysis, psychosynthesis, voice dialogue and neuro-linguistic programming. It is beyond the scope of this book to describe them all in detail, but what they have in common is insistence on taking responsibility for oneself and being willing to become more aware of our unconscious motivations and needs and to change tired old patterns of reacting. These approaches can be experienced either on an individual basis or in groups.

One other course that should be mentioned is Silva Mind Control, a system founded by American Jose Silva which aims to make participants in the four-day course aware of the computer that is their mind and how it can be reprogrammed for better quality of life.

8

TAKING CHARGE OF YOUR ENERGY

Once one starts thinking in terms of energy – or more exactly, becoming tuned into and sensitive to it – life takes on another dimension. Not only will one run less risk of falling ill because of 'overdoing it' because one heeds the warning signs of stress and overwork, but one feels more 'in charge' of what happens to one and less a victim of circumstances. If one is prepared to take responsibility for the energy one puts out, more *quality* and success can be deliberately created in one's life, for energy, like everything else, follows the laws of cause and effect. You do this, and that happens. Much of the misery that plagues us is the result of being unaware of these laws and not living in accordance with them. Remember, energy is neutral: it can work for us or against us.

Here are some propositions that you might try out to test whether they are valid for you or not. My guess is that they will be.

1 Life is a mirror. It is always reflecting US.

There are as many realities as there are people. We create our experience of the world by how we choose to interpret what happens, by what we tell ourselves and the pictures we carry in our minds. And we are always the centre of our own world.

2 Change the *inner*, and the *outer* follows.

Usually what we try to do when things are not going well is to change things (or people) '*out there*'. In relationships, for example, we will go on repeating the same disasters until we get the message that it is something to do with US, and the way WE relate.

3 Attention is energy.
Whatever we dwell on in our thoughts, whatever we brood on,
complain about, we will attract more of to us. We get more of
where we are 'at'.

4 Whatever we resist, persists.
Our likes and dislikes are like strings pulling the objects of our
attachments and aversion to us. If, for example, there is a type of
person you can't stand, you can bet your life that you will keep on
running into these people. They will be everywhere, for you are
carrying them in your consciousness and attracting them to you.

5 What we tell ourselves is supremely important.
Life is impersonal, and tremendously respectful of our freedom to
choose our own reality. If we choose to be victims it will oblige us
by providing victim-like experiences. We are creating our future
by what we think and say NOW.

6 We get back the energy we put out – multiplied.
Negative energy attracts negative energy, positive energy attracts
positive energy. If we try to be positive and loving, we will
surround ourselves with positive and loving people, and attract
good and nourishing experiences to ourselves. If, on the other
hand, we walk about the streets exuding paranoia, we are very
likely to be mugged or have an 'accident'. There are in fact no accidents. We are always responding to each other's energy
vibrations.

7 Your environment is always as high as you are.
How we experience the world is our projection. If we are happy, it
will seem a beautiful place. If we are miserable, we will see misery
everywhere. Heaven and hell are our mind-creations, here now.

8 Choose what you get.
At some level you chose it anyway and are landed with it. Nobody
is a victim. And remember, what you resist, persists.

CREATING QUALITY

One of the things you need to check out is whether you think you *deserve* to have quality in your life. The amount of quality in our lives is always a function of our self-esteem. If you feel you are not worth very much you will tend to be mean with yourself. You will always buy yourself the cheapest clothes, feel guilty if you treat yourself once in a while, not buy yourself the holiday you really would like but decide instead on the 'bargain' being offered. Very commonly, people who are mean with themselves tend to be quite extravagant when it comes to giving to others, buying birthday presents, for example. This is because subconsciously they are trying to buy the affection they are denying to themselves. They hope it will 'come back' to them – and feel disappointed and cheated if it doesn't.

If this is true of you, decide to start being good to yourself. Make a start by caring for your body. Look into a mirror and tell yourself 'I really, really love you – and you deserve the best of everything'. Go to the hairdresser, treat yourself to a sauna and a massage, go out and buy some new clothes. Be a little extravagant – and treat yourself for a change. You will get energy from doing this. And when we know we are looking good, we feel good.

Beautify your surroundings also. Living surrounded by chaos and untidiness (and, even worse, dirt) is guaranteed not to make you feel good. One of the quickest ways to raise and change your energy if you are feeling depressed is to put energy into cleaning up the flat. Hoover, dust, get rid of all that stale washing-up in the kitchen. Play music you like while you do so. Before you know it you will be feeling good again. Install some fresh flowers, and, if you like it, light some incense. If you are redecorating remember that the most restful colours are green and white. Black is depressing, orange and red too stimulating.

GETTING OUT OF THE RUT

Often, feeling low on energy is about *staleness*. Doing the same things in the same way day after day, year in, year out, we can become like robots, doing what we're doing out of sheer habit and without aware-ness. And the more we get entrenched in routine and habit, the more alarming any form of change feels. But change is basically what life is about, and meeting its challenges, though it may be threatening at the time, can be seen in retrospect to have given us a new lease of life. I know a man who felt he was all washed up when, at the age of 55, he was made redundant. He had been in the same job for 15 years. He hadn't really liked it, had to cross the whole city to get from his home to his work and back again, and usually arrived home exhausted in the evening after battling through the rush hour. He applied for many other jobs and was turned down because of his age, before being called for an interview for one that sounded interesting and paid better than the old one. To his own surprise he was offered the job, and loves it. He now has more energy and zest, and actually looks younger. The fact that sometimes he is called at home when disasters occur with the computers does not bother him. In fact he seems to get energy from having to take responsibility and cope with the situation. He feels now that he *matters*.

So if you are feeling perpetually jaded and lack-lustre it may well be that you need a change to stimulate your energy again. What that change will be is up to you. It could be changing your job, or simply trying doing things in a different way. In relationships, for example, you could surprise your partner by not being so predictable all the time. Try taking a few risks and change your pattern. Bring more freshness into your life by doing something new each day – it doesn't necessarily have to be something *big*.

In passing, one should perhaps mention the many opportunities that exist for broadening one's mind in the form of courses. One lady I know who is now a grandmother several times over has resisted the temptation to settle down to a predictable existence of shopping, cooking and cleaning (all of which she is very good at). She signed up for evening classes in bridge and she and her husband now take it in turns with the friends she met there to host bridge parties a couple of times a week in each others' houses. She has made more friends at the Italian classes she attends during the day, and has found time to learn cordon bleu cookery also. She has tremendous energy in spite of being in her sixties and tells me 'this is the best time of my life'. Her husband too is delighted, not only with her cooking, but because at the end of the day they have something to *talk* about.

The list of possible classes one can take are endless. They include not only new skills, but also consciousness-raising groups (for example women's groups, Silva Mind Control) as well as more 'physical' courses that we have already suggested, like aerobics, dance therapy, t'ai chi, aikido . . . Quite apart from boosting your body energy, these will also stimulate you by getting you out of the house and meeting new people. Energy follows the project. Doing something you are interested in and enjoy generates the energy that you will need to perform it. Boredom saps energy, as does stale routine. And, remember, you are only as old as you feel.

PROSPERITY CONSCIOUSNESS

Being mean with yourself and anxious about money comes from the state of mind called 'poverty-consciousness', where there is never enough to go round, not only of money, but everything else as well. Worrying about money never makes you richer. On the contrary, it attracts more of the experience of poverty – and brings your energy down in the process. The more anxious about money one is, the less comes in, or what does, you feel you have to struggle for. Your cheques will be delayed in the post, or you will continually have to be chasing up people who owe you money for your services. If, on the other hand, you think prosperous, little miracles can happen. Money can come from unexpected sources.

Here are some affirmations to help you feel better when you feel lacking, to remind you of the abundance in the universe, and to exchange your panic for trust.

- We always get what we need. I am no exception.
- Money flows towards me. I do not have to struggle to survive.
- I deserve to share in the abundance of the Universe, just for who I am.
- Everything I touch is a success.
- I deserve the best of everything.
- I no longer settle for what I can get, but only for what I want.
- I am richer than I think.

Don't keep telling yourself how poor you are, how on earth are you going to pay your bills and creating catastrophic expectations of the future. Think *prosperous*. And if you have to compare yourself with anybody, do it with people who are worse off than you – and there are certainly plenty of those. You have survived so far – and will continue to do so. And if you are not draining your energy by anxiety you will have more available to help you to do whatever needs to be done to improve your situation.

POSITIVE VISUALISATION

We move towards realising the pictures we carry in our minds. We can make ourselves ill by dwelling on fears of illness, for example, because we are feeding negative thoughts with our attention and thus encouraging them to manifest in our lives.

So, if you are undertaking some new project, visualise its successful completion. For example, if you are being interviewed for promotion or a new job, rehearse in your mind's eye how you would like the interview to go. See yourself fielding the interviewer's questions with ease, and finally being offered the new post. Programme yourself for success and this will bolster your confidence and your energy. Remember, other people relate to us primarily at a vibrational level. They will *feel* whether we are winners or losers. See yourself as a winner and you won't go far wrong. Your whole demeanour will reflect how you feel about yourself.

However nervous you may feel, stop yourself contracting. Breathe deeply while you are waiting. Don't smoke, it will only contract you further. Body language is important. Open up your posture. Uncross your legs and your arms. Make eye contact from time to time (but don't *glare* at your interviewer). Eye contact breeds confidence in social interaction. If we don't look at the other person they will get the impression that we don't like them. And even interviewers like to be liked. Smile, allow a little humour – it will diffuse the tension of the situation. Remember that one of the things passing through the interviewer's mind is whether you can get on with your colleagues – and nobody likes working with a sourpuss.

The most important thing is to feel in your body that you have been successful – *before* actually undertaking the new project. Assume you have, and act as if you have. This 'acting as if' is extraordinarily powerful in making things happen.

THE CREATIVE LAW

Finally, here is a little ritual that brings all these things together. It is called the 'Creative Law' and will attract to you the positive experiences you desire. These are the stages.

1 Decide *exactly* what you want to manifest in your life. Be as detailed as possible, and fix a time within which you want it to happen. Be

clear that you really want whatever it is, and that nobody will suffer from the realisation of your desire. For example, if you need a new flat, decide how many rooms you will need, which area it will be in, which floor it is on, whether there will be a garden etc. See in your imagination your ideal flat, in as much detail as you can. Don't forget the price range, or you may be offered the flat, but at a price you can not afford.

2 Imagine you are hearing a conversation between two of your friends in which they discuss your good fortune and success. What exactly are they saying?

3 Imagine *yourself* breaking the good news to somebody else and receiving their congratulations.

4 Get the feeling in your body that your new abode has in fact already materialised. See yourself already installed and experience how good that feels.

5 Express your gratitude to the universe for meeting your needs.

6 When you feel finished and the energy starts to go out of it, put your flat into a balloon and watch it float away.

7 From now on, assume that it is only a matter of time before your mind creation manifests on the material plane. For example, start checking removals firms in the telephone directory, getting estimates, deciding on colour schemes etc. 'Acting as if' makes things materialise much faster.

You only need to do the creative law once. If you do it more often this only reveals your lack of trust. The exercise depends on *trusting* your own creative power. In moments of doubt, remind yourself that this is in fact the way everything manifests in the world: it starts as an idea in somebody's mind (for example a craftsman's, an architect's, a writer's or composer's) and because they trust that they can do it, they do. Energy follows intention. And don't brag about your powers to others. We all have them, and use them all the time, except that we are usually unaware of our own creations, for good or evil, and either take them for granted or disclaim responsibility for them. If you go around telling everybody what you have done they will very likely think you are a little crazy, or make you doubt your own power to create what you want in your life.

Resist therefore the temptation to keeping digging up the seeds you have planted to see if they are still there. They need to gather strength before they can come into the world, and will do so when they are ripe, rather like flowers (or a baby). It feels like magic and so it is (like flowers or babies). But then energy *is* magic, as well as delight.

9

ENVIRONMENTAL ENERGIES

'No man is an island' said John Donne over 300 years ago. This is as true today as it was then, perhaps even more so. Our globe has shrunk as a result of faster transport and amazing developments in communication. Ideas travel faster and affect the ways in which we think. The population is growing. As the world becomes more densely populated it is harder to escape from other people's vibrations which affect how we feel.

We cannot escape being affected by our environment. You will be in a better position to stay high in energy if you can become more aware of influences in your environment that are draining it.

YOUR HOME ENVIRONMENT

The more restful and pleasing your home environment is, the more you will be able to enjoy it and get some relief from the hurly-burly of your working day. If you know how, you can consciously create a living space for yourself that helps to improve your energy state. On page 105 we looked at the vibrational effects of colours. When you next have to decorate your home, go for green and white which are the most calming (which is why they are used so often in hospitals). Bright colours like reds, oranges and yellows (unless very pale) are too stimulating and more appropriate for a discotheque or a fairground, where the aim is to raise energy. But they are hardly suitable for your living room, or even more, your bedroom. Also avoid blacks, greys and browns which will tend to bring you down, especially on a dark winter's day. If you are feeling a little depressed they will only make you more so. Blues are somewhere in between: cooling, and therefore more suitable for summer than for winter.

Surround yourself with indoor plants. As well as giving you something to nurture (especially if you live alone), their peaceful vibrations will help to calm you down when you stagger in from a heavy working day. If you have no objections to cut flowers, they will soften the vibrations in the room with their beauty and fragrance, as well as supplying one of the best objects of contemplation during your meditation sessions.

Bring nature into your space and draw energy from it, even if it's only a window box. (And, of course, escape into the country or to the seaside as often as you can manage. It's one of the best ways there is of refreshing your spirit.)

Lighting too is important in creating a mood. Overhead lighting can be harsh (quite apart from not making us look our best), and fluorescent lighting is the worst of all. Go for soft, indirect lighting. Spots trained on the ceiling (which will bounce the light back to us) or on pictures or flowers are particularly pleasing.

EVERYDAY POLLUTION

We must all be aware of the dangers of atmospheric pollution, and the damage this can do to our health. Children in particular are at risk from the lead emitted in car exhausts. Whenever we step into a busy street we breathe in poison. The pollution of the atmosphere, rivers and seas, the effects of deforestation without replanting are becoming increasingly accepted as matters of general concern.

What is not so obvious is just how much the pollution in our everyday environment affects our energy systems. Noise affects our stress levels. We are constantly being bombarded by images. The sensory over-stimulation that assails us from seeing countless advertisement hoardings can have a draining effect. Fortunately we can use meditative techniques to counteract this effect once we are sufficiently practised in keeping our energy 'in' by remaining centred by 'holding' a mantra; or practising what in monastic circles is called 'custody of the eyes'. This means being *selective* in what we give our attention to, instead of allowing it to be sucked out on all sides willy-nilly as we walk along a busy street.

ELECTRO-MAGNETIC POLLUTION

What people are only now coming to realise is that pollution affects us every day in more hidden ways – and I am referring here to electro-magnetic pollution.

In his fascinating book *Subtle Energy*, John Davidson quotes the case of the film set that was exposed to radioactive fall-out when the wind changed during a US government nuclear test in the Nevada desert nearly 20 years ago. Since then most of the cast and film-crew have died or are dying of cancer, including John Wayne, Susan Hayward and Clark Gable.

But it is not only nuclear radiation that disturbs the subtle layers of our energy fields where physical and mental deterioration always begin, perhaps long before this manifests in overt symptoms. Several independent research surveys have established that people who live near electricity pylons have a higher than average incidence of suicide and mental illness, as well as leukaemia and other cancers. Recently it was claimed that the emanations from VDUs (Visual Display Units – the screens used in computers and word processors) were causing embryonic deformities and miscarriages in pregnant women who worked with them. It is thought that continued exposure to such electro-magnetic radiation damages our chromosomes and cell reproduction.

We may not be exposed to nuclear fall-out (and, hopefully, never will) or work with computers, but there are television sets in nearly every home. Many of us use microwaves and other domestic appliances like electric shavers and hair-dryers, all of which affect us at this subtle level. Even the telephone, it appears, is suspect; the powerful cobalt magnets used in telephones have been found to affect the functioning of the brain whenever the earpiece is held close to the head. I have often wondered why, after a long (and not necessarily boring) phone conversation, I sometimes have felt quite drained.

There may not be much we can do about removing some of the major sources of energy drain, short of campaigning against the building of nuclear power stations or moving house. After all, we need electric appliances in our homes in order to make our lives easier and more convenient. But what we can do is to ensure, when we finish using them, that these appliances are switched off *at the mains*. We can also discourage our children (or, indeed, ourselves) from becoming 'video junkies', and become aware when watching too much TV is draining us.

Electric appliances are best not sited on our bedside tables if we want to enjoy deep, restful sleep. This applies also to battery-operated watches.

Since everything is interconnected on an energy level, it would be safe to say that *everything* in our environment either gives us more energy – or drains it. It has been found, for example, that living in a house built over water saps the energy of the people living in it. (Paradoxically, living close to water, a lake, say, or a river, actually *gives* us energy.)

THE EFFECT OF SHAPES

Designs and shapes carry their own yin or yang energy which can affect us, our moods and even our health. Your furniture, for example. Sharp edges emit yang energy. Since we need this type of energy in a working situation, austere, straight-backed chairs are appropriate in the office. But in your home this type of furniture will not be conducive to comfort. One sinks more gratefully into chairs and sofas which are soft, yielding and curved, rather than straight-backed.

Shapes therefore have a definite effect on us. To be in a building with a peak, like arches, domes, spires (as in churches and cathedrals), is to feel inspired by the positive energy generated within it.

Pyramids, especially, are powerful energy-transformers. This special energy of the pyramid was first discovered about 60 years ago by a Frenchman named Bovis while he was on holiday in Egypt. While visiting the Great Pyramid he happened to look inside a rubbish bin which contained small dead animals – bats, mice and the odd cat which had got lost in the pyramid and died there of starvation. What struck Bovis as quite remarkable was the fact that these little corpses, though dehydrated, had not decayed.

On his return to France, Bovis experimented with models of pyramids – and found the same phenomenon happening. Later a Czechoslovakian engineer was equally amazed to discover that blunt razor blades kept inside a pyramid overnight were sharp again by morning. The power of the pyramid has not been sufficiently explored to date. It has recently been found, however, that foodstuffs stored in a pyramid will not go mouldy. Interestingly, flies and bacteria show an aversion to entering a pyramid.

A professional healer of my acquaintance swears by pyramids. He has a large, roomy pyramid in his consulting room and conducts healing sessions within it. He keeps another open pyramid over his bed, and claims that since he installed it the quality of his sleep has never been better.

So if you want to increase your positive energy you might like to explore what pyramids can do. If they can make razor blades become as new, they may well do the same for you.

TUNING INTO AURAS

Once you start becoming interested and tuning into the mysteries of energy, everything becomes grist to your mill. You will find that everything has its own aura, its electro-magnetic field, which interacts with your own. Wearing metal on your body, for example, is bad for your energy. This applies not only to jewellery but also to the mercury fillings you may be carrying in your mouth. These are quite toxic. On the other hand, wearing or carrying a crystal is good for energy; crystals are believed by many to be good for our energy.

It is worth taking the trouble to find out about these things. Depending on the type of disturbance being caused in your energy system you could save yourself from a whole range of uncomfortable (and in some cases dire) afflictions. These include heart problems, hypertension, strokes, alcoholism, and migraine (if the disturbance is yang), and low energy and fatigue, malignant and degenerative disorders (eg cancer, multiple sclerosis) if the disturbance is yin.

Yet forewarned is forearmed, and environmental influences can be benign as well as malevolent. The wisdom is to learn the difference – and to go for the positive.

DISPERSING NEGATIVE ENERGY

Here are a few ways to calm yourself down again after being exposed to scattered or negative energy. Try them if you have been in a crowded place or have had a quarrel.

- Shower as soon as you get home. Water is a great conductor of electricity and will wash away those negative vibrations, as well as freshening you up. Remember to wash your hair as well, and finish this cleansing session with a cold shower.

- Energy sticks to clothes, so if you want to change your energy, change your clothes. For preference, wear natural fibres like cotton rather than synthetic materials.

- Wear positive colours. The colour of your clothes also affects your mood. The most positive colours to wear are white (protective), green (the colour of the heart chakra), and orange (the most positive vibrations). Avoid black.

- Aura Cleansing. Many people perform this cleansing ritual just before retiring for the night. They claim that it makes for deeper sleep.

    Using the second and third fingers of both hands, start by pressing firmly on the 'third eye' between the eyebrows. From there, trace a line up and over the crown of the head down to the back of neck and then down the spine as far as you can reach. Still using the same fingers, pick up near the point you left off and continue pressing firmly down the spine, slightly to each side of it, and down the backs of the legs (simultaneously) to the calves. Shake each foot and 'kick off' surplus energy.

    Start again at the third eye, this time with the third and fourth fingers of the right hand. Trace firmly (without forcing) a line up over the scalp and the crown of the head, down the back of the neck, along the left shoulder and the back of the left arm. Finish the movement with a flick, as if you are brushing off the energy.

    Repeat the above, this time using the third and fourth fingers of the left hand and tracing the line over the head and down the back of the right arm.

    Using the third and fourth fingers of both hands, trace the line up from the third eye over the head to a point on the back of the neck between the ears. Here the hands separate, tracing two lines down the neck each side to join together again at the breastbone. Follow the centre line down the front of the body to the pubis. Both hands now simultaneously press firmly down the lines of the front of the legs, finishing with a 'brush off' at the ankles.

    Shake your hands and arms a few times, as if getting rid of drops of water, then shake your body all over to finish off.

<u>CRYSTALS</u>

Crystals have long been believed to have the power to affect our energy in positive ways. Shirley MacLaine swears by them, Tina

Turner won't travel anywhere without hers. Nor would Napoleon without his red carnelian stone.

Crystals were first formed about two million years ago in quartz veins that run through the earth's sandstone layers. In Greek, 'crystallos' means 'petrified light' and in ancient times it was believed that the Gods poured light into the earth and froze it into crystals to help mankind.

It has been established using Kirlian photography that every crystal gives off waves of energy. It is claimed by crystal *afficionados* that, placed near television sets and microwave ovens, they can counteract the low frequency vibrations that over a period of time can leave us feeling really drained. The purifying effect of crystals on water has been established too. Tests have shown that a crystal placed in a glass of tap water affects the molecular structure so that the contents will be as pure as any mountain spring water within an hour. This is probably why animals offered two bowls of water, one crystallised and one not, will only drink from the crystallised water.

The power of crystals to heal and restore flagging energy are also claimed by Soozi Holbeche in her book *The Power of Gems and Crystals*. She suggests that placing a crystal on the thymus area above the heart is a simple and effective way to recharge batteries, just as is holding a crystal in each hand, one with the point towards the elbow and one with the point towards the fingers. This is a good thing to do for example while watching television and the effect is refreshing, rather as if you had plugged into an electric current.

When choosing a crystal for yourself, avoid lead crystals (which may look good but don't do much) and be guided by your own subjective feeling, ie by what you 'pick up' when you handle a particular stone. The more sparkling the crystal, the more stimulating its effect. The darker the colour, the more balanced you will feel by keeping it on you. Rose quartz, it is claimed, is very good for those who have a low self-image and feel vulnerable, while watermelon tourmaline may well help you to keep your relationship together when it seems to be falling apart.

10

REMINDERS

Here is a summary of the things that need to be given attention to if you are to have more energy. Use it as a check list to become aware of just *how* you may be allowing yourself to get drained, or simply why you don't have the energy available that you would like.

1 Eat (and drink) wisely and well – but not *too* well.
2 Breathe efficiently. Make sure you are getting enough fresh air and appropriate exercise.
3 Get enough sleep and replenish your stores of energy by structuring sessions of alpha during the day (eg meditation, deep relaxation). Give yourself time and space.
4 Stay in touch with your own energy process and biorhythms so you don't drain yourself by overdoing things.
5 Be wary of overcommitting yourself. Set yourself priorities and manage your time and space more efficiently.
6 Stay centred in your body rather than in your head. Open out your body posture. Expand, rather than contract.
7 Be aware of when you are allowing negativity to bring you down – whether your own or other people's. Stay positive – especially about yourself.
8 Enjoy what you do, and do what you enjoy. Resistance saps your energy, so if you have agreed to do something, do it totally, willingly. Don't be a victim.
9 Become more aware of toxic influences in your environment. Practise sense withdrawal when feeling over-stimulated and over-exposed. Choose to let in only nourishing energy – and people. Regularly clear your aura – and work too on clearing your 'unfinished business' so your 'buttons' are not continually being pushed.

10 Stop bringing yourself down with worry and catastrophic expectations. Learn to trust. The Universe is on *your* side.

The underlying assumptions of this book, running through all the tips, structures and techniques we have described, have been:

1 That we have the power to transform our energy (if we learn how), rather than being stuck with what we get.
2 That the *responsibility* for the quality of your life (which is the same as saying that the energies you experience in your life) are your own creation. They are a function of *you*. You are always the boss.
3 That energy, like everything else, follows the laws of cause and effect. You do this, and this happens. Much of the unhappiness in people's lives is the result of not being aware of these laws. With more awareness of the karmic effect of our thoughts and actions we will have a happier time on this planet. We can either enjoy the ride on this roller coaster that is Life – or be dragged along by it.

This heightened awareness includes that of the yin and yang of Existence as they manifest in our daily lives. There is a time for creating new things – and a time for surrendering to what is, and allowing oneself to flow with it. Understanding this difference is the beginning of wisdom.

BIBLIOGRAPHY

Dr Herbert Benson *The Relaxation Response* (Collins 1976)

Eric Berne *Games People Play* (Penguin 1970)

John Davidson *Subtle Energy* (C. W. Daniel Company Ltd 1987)

Shakti Gawain *Creative Visualisation* (Bantam Books 1987)

Soozi Holbeche *The Power of Gems and Crystals* (Piatkus 1990)

Leslie and Susannah Kenton *Raw Energy* (Century Arrow 1986)

Lucinda Lidell *The Book of Massage* (Ebury Press 1984)

Lucinda Lidell and The Sivananda Yoga Centre *The Book of Yoga* (Ebury Press 1983)

Alexander Lowen *The Language of the Body* (Collier Macmillan 1971)

Toru Namikoshi *Shiatsu Therapy* (Japan Publications Inc 1974)

Louis Proto *Meditation for Everybody* (Penguin 1991)
  Total Relaxation (The Alpha Plan) (Penguin 1989)
  Who's Pulling Your Strings? (Thorsons 1989)

Wilhelm Reich *The Sexual Revolution* (Vision Press 1969)

Bernie Siegel *Love, Medicine and Miracles* (Century Arrow 1989)

Dr Carl Simonton *Getting Well Again* (Bantam Books 1986)

Monika Struna and Connie Church *Self Massage* (Century 1987)

Tom and Carole Valentine *Applied Kinesiology* (Thorsons 1985)

Michael Weiner *Maximum Immunity* (Gateway Books 1986)

USEFUL ADDRESSES

The Dr Edward Bach Centre
Mount Vernon
Sotwell
Wallingford
Oxon OX10 0PZ

The British Acupuncture Council
Park House
206 Latimer Road
London W10 6RE

The College of Traditional Acupuncture
Tao House
Queensway
Leamington Spa
Warwickshire CV31 3LZ

British T'ai Chi Chuan Centre
208 Maybank Road
London E18

The International Rolf Institute
PO Box 1868
Boulder
Colorado 80306
USA

Society of Teachers of the Alexander Technique
20 London House
266 Fulham Road
London SW10 9EL

The Association of Kinesiology
39 Browns Road
Surbiton
Surrey KT5 8ST

Mysteries Book Shop
9–11 Monmouth Street
Covent Garden
London WC2H 9DA

INDEX